W. B. SAUNDERS COMPANY
Philadelphia London Toronto
Mexico City Rio de Janeiro
Sydney Tokyo

WORKBOOK TO ACCOMPANY Modern Dental Assisting

THIRD EDITION

Hazel O. Torres, C.D.A., R.D.A., M.A.

Ann Ehrlich, C.D.A., M.A.

Illustrated by Stephen Michael Rizzuto, B.A., M.A.

W. B. Saunders Company: West Washington Square
Philadelphia, PA 19105

Workbook to accompany Modern Dental Assisting   ISBN   0-7216-1528-7

Last digit is the print number: 9 8 7 6 5 4 3

TABLE OF CONTENTS

TABLE OF CONTENTS (continued)

TO THE STUDENT:

This workbook has been written to help you learn! Learning goals, exercises and criteria sheets have been developed to best suit the material presented in each chapter and to make it easier for you to master learning and apply the content.

Neither the textbook, nor this workbook, is definitive in itself. The authors strongly encourage both students and instructors to use the many additional reference materials which are available to enrich the student's comprehension and ultimate performance as a dental assistant. Some of these references are listed at the end of each chapter in the text.

LEARNING GOALS

A learning goal is a statement of what the student will be able to do upon successful completion of an area of study.

In the limited space available it would be impossible to include a definitive list of all the goals for all the chapters. Therefore, the authors have selected those goals which we believe are most important for each chapter.

There are many important learning goals which could not be included on this list and your instructor may add some of these goals for each chapter.

The purpose of including learning goals is to provide guidelines to help you identify the most important areas as you study each chapter; however, the most important learning goals are the ones you set for yourself!

EXERCISES

The exercises included in this workbook are an important part of your learning experience. Please take time to work through them carefully. The questions are in a multiple choice format. Your concern is to select the best answer from the choices offered. The correct answer to each question can be found in the text.

These are not intended as test questions! Instead they are planned to help you study, interact with and better understand the information presented in the text.

CRITERIA SHEETS

The use of the term "criteria" in education states that there are standards established for acceptable performance of an observable procedure. The authors have included criteria for specific procedures to assist you in achieving these acceptable standards.

Learning objective self-evaluation is important because once you are working in an actual dental practice you will be responsible for maintaining your skills and the quality of your work. To help you learn to do this, each criteria page includes space for you to evaluate your own performance as you practice the procedure.

Space is also provided for evaluation by your instructor. This provides feedback as to whether or not you have actually mastered the criteria. In the criteria sheets we have used the following coding: Criterion met = C; Criterion not met = X.

IN CONCLUSION

The authors hope this workbook will be a meaningful aid to you, the student, as you pursue your studies to enable you to enter the profession of dental assisting.

Hazel O. Torres   Ann Ehrlich

CHAPTER 1   THE HISTORY OF DENTISTRY

LEARNING GOALS

The student will be able to:

1. Identify early developments and major contributors to dentistry
   from early times through the Middle Ages and the Renaissance.

2. Identify the pioneers in dentistry in the United States.

3. Trace the development of dentistry in the United States and
   identify the contributors to this growth.

4. Describe the effect of the Amalgam War on the history of
   organized dentistry in the United States.

5. List the major other developments in dentistry and identify their
   innovators.

EXERCISES

Match the following names and titles:

1. _____ Hippocrates   (a) The founder of modern dentistry

2. _____ Andreas Vesalius   (b) The founder of modern surgery

3. _____ Pierre Fauchard   (c) The father of medicine

4. _____ Greene Vardiman Black   (d) The grand old man in dentistry

                                   (e) The founder of modern anatomy

5. The _____ is one of the oldest known medical works containing
   references to dentistry. It is reported to have been written
   about 2700 B.C.

   (a) Canon of Medicine
   (b) De Medicina
   (c) Ebers Papyrus
   (d) Law of the Twelve Tables

6. In _____ the first dental school in the world was opened in Baltimore, Md.

    (a) 1805
    (b) 1826
    (c) 1840
    (d) 1857

Match the following:

7. _____ John Greenwood   (a) A pioneer in dental education.

8. _____ Horace H. Hayden   (b) Introduced the doctrine of extension for prevention.

9. _____ Crawcour brothers   (c) Introduced amalgam in the United States as "royal mineral succedaneum."

10. _____ G.V. Black   (d) Dentist to George Washington.

                                 (e) Introduced the gold inlay.

11. _____ is said to have hired the first dental assistant and was a pioneer in dental radiography (x-rays).

    (a) Edward Angle
    (b) Alfred C. Fones
    (c) Chapin Harris
    (d) C. Edmund Kells

12. _____ was the first to use the term <u>caries</u> and to reject the idea that caries was caused by "worms of the teeth."

    (a) Abulcasis
    (b) John Baker
    (c) Pierre Fauchard
    (d) Lucy Hobbs Taylor

13. The dental engine was introduced _____.

    (a) before 1800.
    (b) in the late 1840's.
    (c) in the 1870's.
    (d) after 1920.

14. _____ introduced the use of rubber dam.

    (a) Robert A. Arthur
    (b) Sanford C. Barnum
    (c) G.V. Black
    (d) Wm. H. Taggart
    (e) Horace Wells

15. Which of the following statement(s) is/are true about the amalgam war?

    (a) Amalgam was introduced by Chapin Harris in 1843.
    (b) In 1856, M. Taveau recommended a ban on the use of amalgam in the United States.
    (c) Amalgam was not commonly accepted until significant improvements were made by Tomes, Black and others.
    (d) The Crawcour brothers invented amalgam in 1826.
    (e) None of the above

16. _____ held the view that men had more teeth than women.

    (a) Aristotle
    (b) Cornelius Celsus
    (c) Claudius Galen
    (d) Scrapion

17. _____ is considered to be the first native-born American dentist.

    (a) John Baker
    (b) Isaac Greenwood, Sr.
    (c) John Greenwood
    (d) John Hunter

18. The first dental society in the United States was organized by the dentists of _____ in 1834.

    (a) Maryland
    (b) Massachusetts
    (c) New Jersey
    (d) New York

19. _____ demonstrated that there is no circulation of blood in dentin or enamel.

    (a) Edward Angle
    (b) Sanford C. Barnum
    (c) G. V. Black
    (d) Sir John Tomes

20. _____ was the leading material for filling molar cavities from the 1870's until 1907.

    (a) Amalgam
    (b) Cast gold
    (c) Cohesive gold foil
    (d) Gutta percha

21. _____ wrote Le Chirurgien Dentiste.

    (a) Cornelius Celsus
    (b) Pierre Fauchard
    (c) Claudius Galen
    (c) Andreas Vesalius

22. _____ introduced the doctrine of extension for prevention.

    (a) Robert Arthur
    (b) G. V. Black
    (b) C. Edmund Kells
    (d) Conrad Roentgen

23. The use of nitrous oxide anesthesia in dentistry was introduced by _____.

    (a) Sanford C. Barnum
    (b) William T. G. Morton
    (c) William H. Taggart
    (d) Horace Wells

24. _____ was the first dentist to hire a dental assistant.

    (a) G. V. Black
    (b) John Greenwood
    (c) C. Edmund Kells
    (d) Paul Revere

25. _____ was the first author to speak of the nerves of the teeth.

    (a) Cornelius Celsus
    (b) Claudius Galen
    (c) Hippocrates
    (d) Scrapion

LEARNING GOALS

The student will be able to:

1. List, and describe briefly, the eight dental specialties.

2. Discuss the responsibilities, education, licensure certification, registration, and professional organization as applicable for the dentist, dental assistant, hygienist, and laboratory technician.

3. Identify 10 potential expanded functions that may be assigned to dental auxiliaries.

4. Define or describe the following: ethics; jurisprudence; State Dental Practice Act; unlicensed practice of dentistry; respondeat superior; res gestae, malpractice; and reasonable skill, care and judgement.

5. Identify the following: ADA, ADAA, CDA, CDT, DDS, DMD, EFDA, RDA and RDH.

EXERCISES

1. The expanded functions assigned to qualified dental auxiliaries are controlled by the ADA National Board of Dentistry.

   (a) true
   (b) false

2. _____ is that part of philosophy that deal with moral conduct, duty, and judgment. It is concerned with standards for judging whether actions are right or wrong.

   (a) Ethics
   (b) Jurisprudence
   (c) Res gestae
   (d) Respondeat superior

3. The national certification examination for dental assistants is given by the _____.

   (a) American Dental Association National Board of Dentistry.
   (b) Certifying Board of the ADA.
   (c) Dental Assisting National Board.
   (d) National Board of the American Dental Assistants Association.

4. Malpractice is _____.

   (a) acts of omission and acts of commission.
   (b) failure to act as a "reasonable and prudent man."
   (c) performing acts that a "reasonable and prudent man"
       would not perform.
   (d) professional negligence.
   (e) all of the above

5. The doctrine of respondeat superior holds true even if the
   employee is specially licensed, such as an RDA or an RDH.

   (a) true
   (b) false

Match the following:

6. _____ ADA   (a) American Denturist Association

7. _____ ADAA   (b) American Dental Assistants
                                     Association

8. _____ CDA   (c) Registered Dental Hygienist

9. _____ RDH   (d) Registered Dental Assistant

10. _____ RDA   (e) American Dental Association

                                 (f) Certified Dental Assistant

                                 (g) Current Dental Assistant

11. _____ is the science dealing with law applied to dentistry.
    This term is used to include statutes regulating the legal
    aspects of the practice of dentistry.

    (a) Dental jurisprudence
    (b) Ethics
    (c) Malpractice
    (d) Respondeat superior

12. A _____ is a dental technician who fabricates and fits dentures
    directly for patients with or without a written prescription
    from a dentist.

    (a) CDT
    (b) denturist
    (c) DMD
    (d) EFDA

13. The principle of "reasonable skill, care and judgement" applies only to the dentist and licensed auxiliaries and does not apply to dental assistants.

    (a) true
    (b) false

14. In each state, the _____ contains the legal restrictions and controls on the dentist, dental auxiliaries, and the practice of dentistry.

    (a) ADA Code of Ethics
    (b) Federal Principles of Ethics
    (c) State Board of Dentistry
    (d) State Dental Practice Act

15. Under the concept of _____, statements spontaneously made by anyone at the time of an alleged negligent act are admissible as evidence and may be damaging to the interests of the dentist.

    (a) professional negligence
    (b) res gestae
    (c) respondeat superior
    (d) the prudent man

16. When the patient enters a dentist's office he gives _____ consent, at least for the dental examination.

    (a) applied
    (b) implied
    (c) verbal
    (d) written

Match the following terms and definitions:

17. _____ Prosthodontist

(a) Treats disease of the dental pulp, usually with root-canal therapy.

18. _____ Oral Surgeon

(b) Works as a public educator in the prevention of dental disease.

19. _____ Endodontist

(c) Fits and designs bridgework and dentures to replace missing teeth.

20. _____ Periodontist

(d) Treats injuries, diseases and deformities of the mouth and face and performs extractions.

(e) Treats gum disease.

21. Before being eligible to sit for the certification examination,
    the assistant must _____.

    (a) have 5 years of work experience.
    (b) hold current cardiopulmonary resuscitation (CPR)
        certification.
    (c) pass a state licensure examination.
    (d) A and C

22. In some states, applying topical anesthetics is an expanded
    function which is assigned to the _____.

    (a) administrative assistant
    (b) coordinating assistant
    (c) denturist
    (d) EFDA

23. The assistant must make every effort to understand the patient
    and his needs.

    (a) true
    (b) false

24. Engaging in the unlicensed practice of dentistry is a _____.

    (a) criminal act
    (b) felony
    (c) misdemeanor
    (d) res gestae

25. A _____ is the standard of moral principle and practice to which
    a profession adheres.

    (a) code of ethics
    (b) code of licensure
    (c) principles of registry
    (d) state dental practice act

LEARNING GOALS

The student will be able to:

1. Identify the body systems in terms of structure (components) and function.

2. Identify the bones and major anatomic landmarks of the skull.

3. Describe the histology of bone in terms of: cartilage, compact bone, spongy bone, and the periosteum.

4. Describe the glide and hinge action of the temporomandibular joint.

5. Identify the major muscles of mastication, facial expression, the floor of the mouth, extrinsic muscles of the tongue, and major posterior muscles of the mouth.

6. Identify the major veins and arteries of the face and mouth.

7. Identify the major sources of innervation of the teeth and oral cavity.

8. Identify the major anatomic landmarks of the oral cavity.

9. Name and locate the salivary glands and their ducts.

10. List the major lymph nodes of the face and neck.

EXERCISES

Match the following systems and components:

1. _____ Digestive system   (a) Paranasal sinuses

2. _____ Endocrine system   (b) Tissue fluid

3. _____ Nervous system   (c) Esophagus

4. _____ Respiratory system   (d) Special sense organs

5. _____ Lymphatic system   (e) Gonads

                                   (f) Parathyroids

6. The _____ is the connective tissue which covers the outside of
the bone. It is necessary for bone growth and repair.

(a) cancellous tissue
(b) haversian system
(c) hematopoietic tissue
(d) periosteum

7. The _____ salivary glands lie subcutaneously just in front of,
and below, each ear.

(a) frontal
(b) parotid
(c) sublingual
(d) submandibular

Match the following muscles and functions:

8. _____ Buccinator

(a) Raises and wrinkles the skin of
the chin and pushes up the lower
lip.

9. _____ Masseter

(b) Serves to compress the cheeks,
hold food in contact with the
teeth, and retract the angles
of the mouth.

10. _____ Orbicularis Oris

(c) Acts to close the jaws. Its
origin is in the temporal fossa
and its insertion is at the
anterior border of the ramus and
the coronoid process of the
mandible.

11. _____ Temporal

(d) Acts to close the jaws. It
originates from the zygomatic
arch and inserts on the outer
(lateral) surface of the ramus
and the angle of the mandible.

(e) It is made up of many layers of
fibers surrounding the mouth.
Its insertion is at the angles
of the mouth.

12. The _____ form(s) a protective lymphoid tissue barrier for the mouth, throat, larynx, trachea, and lungs.

    (a) paranasal sinuses
    (b) suprarenals
    (c) thyroid
    (d) tonsils

13. The _____ artery enters the face at the inferior border of the mandible. It can be detected by gently palpating the mandibular notch.

    (a) aorta
    (b) facial
    (c) maxillary
    (d) mandibular

Match the following bones and descriptions:

14. _____ Mandible

15. _____ Ethmoid

16. _____ Temporal

17. _____ Zygomatic

(a) Forms the sides and base of the cranium.

(b) Forms the forehead, most of the orbital roof and the anterior cranial floor.

(c) Is the principal supporting structure of the nasal cavity.

(d) Forms the lower jaw. It is the strongest and longest bone of the face.

(e) Prominence of the cheeks and part of the lateral wall and floor of the orbits

18. In the temporomandibular joint, the _____ action is the second phase in mouth opening and movement. This phase consists of a movement of the _____ and meniscus forward and downward along the articular eminence.

    (a) gliding   capsular ligament
    (b) gliding   condyle
    (c) hinge   condyle
    (d) hinge   glenoid fossa

19. Blood pressure is the highest at the time of contraction of the ventricles and is called _____ pressure.

    (a) diastolic
    (b) systolic

20. The taste buds are located within the _____, which are the numerous small projections found on the tongue.

    (a) aponeurosis
    (b) dendrites
    (c) lymphocytes
    (d) papillae

Match the following nerves and areas of innervation:

21. _____   Maxillary centrals   (a) Posterior superior alveolar
                                             nerve

22. _____   Mucoperiosteum of   (b) Mental nerve
              the mandibular molars

23. _____   Mandibular cuspid   (c) Anterior superior alveolar nerve

24. _____   Maxillary second   (d) Incisive nerve
              molar

25. _____   Maxillary first   (e) Buccal nerve
              premolars

                                        (f) Middle superior alveolar nerve

26. The spleen, thymus and tonsils are part of the _____ system.

    (a) excretory
    (b) lymphatic
    (c) nervous
    (d) reproductive

27. The _____ are the largest of the paranasal sinuses and are located in the maxilla.

    (a) ethmoid
    (b) frontal
    (c) maxillary
    (d) sphenoid

28. The maxillary division of the _____ nerve supplies the maxillary teeth.

   (a) mylohyoid
   (b) nasopalatine
   (c) ophthalmic
   (d) trigeminal

29. _____ is the enzyme responsible for the formation of fibrin in the formation of a blood clot.

   (a) Anabolism
   (b) Insulin
   (c) Ptyalin
   (d) Thrombin

30. The _____ is a free projection hanging from the posterior end of the soft palate. When stimulated it activates the gag reflex.

   (a) epiglottis
   (b) incisive papilla
   (c) rugae
   (d) uvula

Match the following anatomic landmarks and definitions:

31. _____ Condyle

32. _____ Foramen

33. _____ Fossa

34. _____ Sinus

35. _____ Suture

(a) An opening through which blood vessels, nerves and ligaments pass.

(b) An articulation in which the bones are united by a thin layer of fibrous tissue.

(c) Any marked bony prominence or projection.

(d) A rounded or knuckle-like prominence, usually found at the point of articulation with another bone.

(e) A depression or cavity in or on a bone.

(f) A cavity within a bone.

36. The _____ of the lips respresents a zone of transition from skin to mucous membrane.

    (a) frenum
    (b) labial vestibule
    (c) philtrum
    (d) vermilion border

37. The inside of the cheeks, vestibule and lips are covered with _____.

    (a) lamina propria
    (b) lining mucosa
    (c) masticatory mucosa
    (d) specialized mucosa

38. The _____ is/are a series of mucosal ridges which occur on the anterior portion of the hard palate just behind the maxillary incisors.

    (a) fauces
    (b) frenum
    (c) rugae
    (d) symphysis

39. _____ is the process by which nutrients are actually put to use by the body.

    (a) Anabolism
    (b) Catabolism
    (c) Digestion
    (d) Metabolism

40. _____ are the components of the endocrine gland which produce insulin.

    (a) Gonads
    (b) Pancreatic Islets
    (c) Parathyroids
    (d) Suprarenals

41. _____ is/are the opening into the mouth for the parotid salivary glands.

    (a) Ducts of Rivinus
    (b) Posterior ducts
    (c) Stensen's duct
    (d) Wharton's duct

42. A _____ is a narrow fold of mucous membrane passing from a more fixed to a movable part.

    (a) fauce
    (b) frenum
    (b) philtrum
    (d) vestibule

43. There are no digestive enzymes in the large intestine.

    (a) true
    (b) false

Match the following terms and definitions:

44. _____ Anterior   (a) A plane vertically dividing the body into left and right halves.

45. _____ Posterior   (b) Toward the front.

46. _____ Midsagittal   (c) Toward the midline.

47. _____ Distal   (d) Away from the midline.

                             (e) Toward the back.

48. The major blood supply to the mandibular teeth is from the _____.

    (a) anterior artery
    (b) inferior alveolar arteries
    (c) lingual artery
    (d) A and C

49. The _____ in an infected area tend to become swollen and tender.

    (a) arterioles
    (b) lymph ducts
    (c) lymph nodes
    (d) veins

50. The facial nerve innervates the _____ muscle(s).

    (a) buccinator
    (b) orbicularis oris
    (c) zygomatic major
    (d) all of the above

OPTIONAL PRACTICE

You may wish to use the diagram below to test your ability to identify these structures.

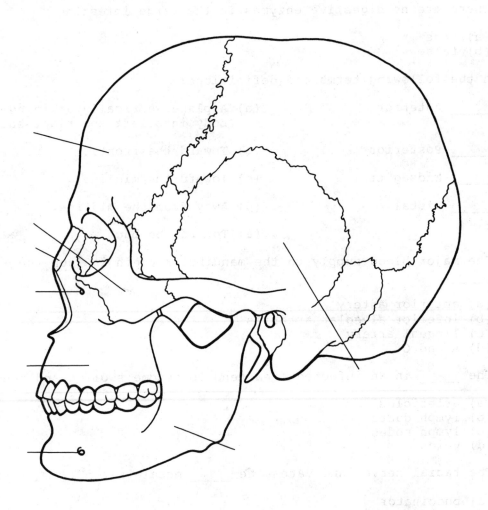

OPTIONAL PRACTICE

You may wish to use the diagram below to test your ability to
identify these structures.

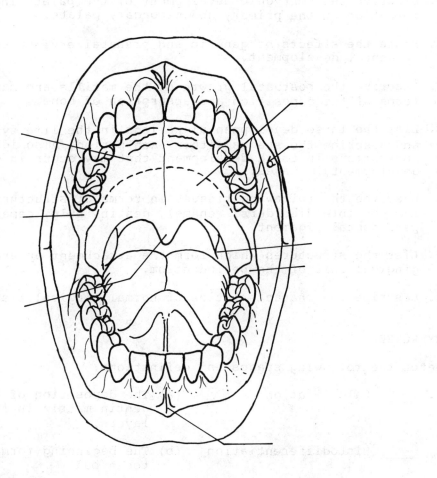

LEARNING GOALS

The student will be able to:

1. Name the three primary embryonic layers and describe the tissues
   each forms following differentiation.

2. Describe the embryonic development of the palate including
   formation of the primary and secondary palate.

3. State the effects of genetic and prenatal environmental factors
   on dental development.

4. Describe the postnatal growth of the maxilla and mandible in
   terms of the deposition and absorption of bone.

5. List the three developmental periods in the life cycle of a tooth
   and describe the stages within each period. Also identify the
   aberrations in tooth development that may occur in each of these
   developmental stages.

6. Describe the following tissues in terms of structure, function
   and possible disorders: enamel, dentin, pulp, cementum, and
   periodontal ligament.

7. List the structures which form the attachment apparatus and the
   gingival unit of the periodontium.

8. Describe the characteristics of normal gingival tissue.

EXERCISES

Match the following stages and definitions:

1. _____ Calcification

2. _____ Histodifferentiation

3. _____ Initiation

4. _____ Morphodifferentiation

(a) The deposition of the enamel and
    dentin matrix in incremental
    layers.

(b) The beginning formation of the
    tooth bud.

(c) The depositing of calcium salts
    in the enamel and dentin matrix.

(d) The specialization of cells.

(e) The arrangement of cells in the
    pattern of the future tooth.

5. The _____ differentiates into the epithelium; brain and spinal cord; hair and nails; enamel of the teeth; and the lining of the oral cavity.

   (a) branchial arches
   (b) ectoderm
   (c) entoderm
   (d) mesoderm

6. During the fifth and sixth weeks the _____ of the embryo is formed by the union of the medial nasal process and the lateral nasal processes.

   (a) palatal shelves
   (b) primary palate
   (c) secondary palate
   (d) soft palate

7. The primary genetic factor of most common concern in dental development is a serious discrepancy in the size and relationship of teeth and jaws.

   (a) true
   (b) false

8. After birth, the palate grows downward by the _____ of bone on its undersurface and the _____ of bone in the nasal area.

   (a) absorption   deposition
   (b) apposition   resorption
   (c) deposition   apposition
   (d) resorption   apposition

Match the following developmental disturbance and definitions:

9. _____ Amelogenesis   (a) A union between the dentin and
          Imperfecta   enamel of two or more separate
                                   developing teeth.

10. _____ Anodontia   (b) A congenital absence of teeth.

11. _____ Enamel hypoplasia   (c) An abnormality in which the
                                   enamel formation and/or
                                   calcification is defective.

12. _____ Fusion   (d) A defect in which the enamel
                                   remains in the matrix stage.

                              (e) A deficient formation of the
                                   enamel matrix.

13. The _____ are the enamel producing cells.

    (a) ameloblasts
    (b) cementoblasts
    (c) dentinoblasts
    (d) odontoblasts

14. Which of the following statement(s) is/are true of enamel?

    (a) The structural units of enamel are called perikymata.
    (b) Enamel is composed of millions of calcified enamel rods
        or prisms.
    (c) Enamel is flexible.
    (d) Enamel is the hardest calcified tissue in the body.
    (e) B and D

15. The teeth are supported in their functional positions in the
    jaws by the _____ which is the extension of the bone of the body
    of the mandible and maxilla.

    (a) alveolar process
    (b) attachment apparatus
    (c) epithelial attachment
    (d) periodontal ligament

Match the following bones and descriptions:

16. _____ Cortical Plate   (a) The thin, compact bone lining
                                  the tooth socket.

17. _____ Lamina Dura   (b) The alveolar bone separating the
                                  roots of the teeth.

18. _____ Trabeculae   (c) The dense outer bone which
                                  provides strength and
                                  protection.

                              (d) The spongy bone making up the
                                  central portion of the alveolar
                                  process.

19. Which of the following statement(s) is/are true of the dentin?

    (a) Dentin is formed by the ameloblasts.
    (b) Dentin contains Hunter-Schreger bands.
    (c) Primary dentin is formed prior to the eruption of the tooth.
    (d) The hardness of dentin is known to be less than that of enamel, but is greater than that of bone.
    (e) C and D

20. _____ grows by the apposition of new layers, one on another. It is this characteristic that makes orthodontic treatment possible.

    (a) Cementum
    (b) Dentin
    (c) Enamel
    (d) Predentin

21. The _____ is a pear-shaped structure formed of dense connective tissue and located directly posterior to the maxillary central incisors.

    (a) incisive canal
    (b) incisive papilla
    (c) palatine raphe
    (d) palatine rugae

22. The _____ is the space between the free gingiva and the tooth. When healthy it rarely exceeds 2.5 mm in depth.

    (a) epithelial attachment
    (b) free gingiva
    (c) gingival margin
    (d) gingival sulcus

23. The mandible and the maxillary floor of the orbits are formed from the _____.

    (a) first branchial arch
    (b) second branchial arch
    (c) third branchial arch
    (d) stomodeum

24. _____ is the normal process by which the primary teeth are shed.

    (a) Eruption
    (b) Exfoliation
    (c) Morphodifferentiation
    (d) Proliferation

25. The _____ teeth are those permanent teeth which replace the primary teeth.

    (a) germination
    (b) milk
    (c) succedaneous
    (d) twinning

26. The roots of the primary teeth are normally resorbed by the _____.

    (a) ameloclasts
    (b) cementoblasts
    (c) odontoblasts
    (d) osteoclasts

27. The _____ fibers prevent tipping of the tooth.

    (a) alveolar
    (b) apical
    (c) oblique
    (d) transseptal

28. The _____ palate is formed by the union of the medial nasal process with the lateral nasal processes.

    (a) primary
    (b) secondary
    (c) soft
    (d) B and C

29. _____ means division into three roots.

    (a) Apex
    (b) Bifurcation
    (c) Trifurcation
    (d) none of the above

30. The normal duration of human gestation is _____ lunar months.

    (a) 8
    (b) 9
    (c) 10
    (d) 11

OPTIONAL PRACTICE

You may wish to use the diagram below to test your ability to
identify these structures.

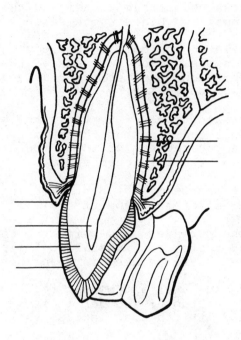

LEARNING GOALS

The student will be able to:

1. Identify the four types of teeth, describe the design and specialized functions of each type, and classify them as anterior or posterior teeth.

2. Describe the Universal Numbering System and the Federation Dentaire International Two-Digit Tooth-Recording System.

3. Define the terms related to tooth morphology including: the curve of Spee, the names of the surfaces of the teeth, contours and contacts, overbite and overjet, embrasure and occlusal form and the physiology of occlusion.

4. Identify the number and types of teeth in the primary dentition; state the specialized functions of the primary dentition and describe the special characters of these teeth such as enamel thickness and size of the pulp chamber.

5. Compare the primary and permanent dentition in terms of: numbers and types of teeth; size and shape of similar types of teeth.

6. Identify each of the permanent and primary teeth in terms of number of cusps and roots, and unusual anatomic landmarks. The correct terminology should be used in describing these landmarks.

7. Given an extracted tooth, or a typodont tooth, identify the following: the type of tooth; whether it is an anterior or posterior tooth; and if it has an incisal edge or an occlusal surface.

EXERCISES

1. _____ is the horizontal overlap of the maxillary teeth.

   (a) Overbite
   (b) Overjet

2. Using the _____ tooth number system, the primary teeth are lettered using capital letters A through T.

   (a) International
   (b) Palmer
   (c) Symbolic
   (d) Universal

3. Each tooth in the dental arch has two antagonists in the opposing
   arch except the _____ and the _____.

   (a) mandibular centrals   maxillary third molars
   (b) mandibular premolars   mandibular centrals
   (c) maxillary centrals   mandibular third molars
   (d) maxillary laterals   maxillary third molars

Answer these questions based on the drawings below.

4. This is a/an _____ tooth.

   (a) cuspid
   (b) incisor
   (c) molar
   (d) premolar

5. This is a/an _____ tooth.

   (a) anterior
   (b) posterior

6. This is a/an _____ tooth.

   (a) cuspid
   (b) incisor
   (c) molar
   (d) premolar

7. This is a/an _____ tooth.

   (a) anterior
   (b) posterior

8. The tooth shown in drawing #5 is a/an _____.

   (a) cuspid
   (b) incisor
   (c) molar
   (d) premolar

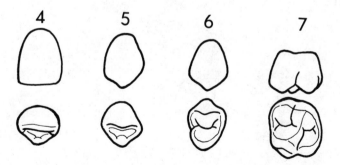

9. The _____ is the V-shaped space between two adjoining teeth in contact in the same arch.

   (a) cingulum
   (b) contact point
   (c) embrasure
   (d) proximal point

10. A concave surface is one that is slightly rounded _____.

   (a) inwardly
   (b) outwardly

Match the following surfaces and definitions:

11. _____ Buccal surface

(a) The surface of an anterior tooth positioned immediately adjacent to the lip.

12. _____ Distal surface

(b) That surface of the tooth facing toward the midline.

13. _____ Lingual surface

(c) That surface of a posterior tooth positioned immediately adjacent to the cheek.

14. _____ Mesial surface

(d) The surface of a tooth facing away from the midline.

(e) That surface of the tooth which faces toward the tongue.

15. A _____ is that angle formed by the junction of two surfaces of a tooth crown along an imaginary line.

   (a) binangle
   (b) line angle
   (c) point angle
   (d) triangle

16. Which of the following statement(s) is/are true regarding the primary dentition?

    (a) Contains no premolars.
    (b) The pulp chamber is relatively large.
    (c) The teeth are short and squat in appearance and milk-white in color.
    (d) A and C
    (e) A, B and C

17. _____ surfaces are those tooth surfaces which are adjacent to each other in the same arch.

    (a) Axial
    (b) Incisal
    (c) Labial
    (d) Proximal

18. The maxillary first molar has _____ roots.

    (a) 1
    (b) 2
    (c) 3
    (d) 4

Match the following terms and definitions:

19. _____ Cingulum

20. _____ Cusp of Carabelli

21. _____ Lingual fossa

22. _____ Mamelon

(a) The "fifth" cusp located on the lingual surface of many maxillary first molars.

(b) A broad, shallow depression on the lingual surface of an incisor or cuspid.

(c) A bulge or prominence of enamel found on the cervical third of the lingual surface of an anterior tooth.

(d) A linear elevation on the surface of a tooth. It is named according to its location or form.

(e) A rounded or conical prominence on the incisal ridge of a newly erupted incisor.

23. _____ is/are the contact between the maxillary and mandibular teeth in all mandibular positions and movements.

    (a) Extrusion
    (b) Interproximation
    (c) Occlusion
    (d) Quadrants

24. A _____ is formed when two fissures cross.

    (a) cusp
    (b) fossa
    (c) mamelon
    (d) pit

25. There are _____ premolars in the primary dentition.

    (a) 0
    (b) 2
    (c) 4
    (d) 8

PROCEDURE: PRELIMINARY IDENTIFICATION OF PERMANENT TEETH

Note: This is an entry level skill. Students are expected to
      continue improving their skills until they can identify any
      tooth in the permanent or primary dentition and state
      whether it comes from the maxillary or mandibular arch.

GOAL: Given a typodont, or extracted teeth, the student will
      identify each tooth as to the type of tooth it is; and
      classify each as to whether it is an anterior or a posterior
      tooth.

SE = Student evaluation C = Criterion met IE = Instructor evaluation X = Criterion not met	SE	IE
1. **Instruments and Materials:** a typodont (model with removable teeth) or extracted teeth.		
2. Sorted teeth into groups by type of tooth. (Incisors, cuspids, premolars and molars)		
3. Divided these groups into anterior and posterior teeth.		
Comments:		

CHAPTER 6 MICROBIOLOGY AND STERILIZATION

LEARNING GOALS

The student will be able to:

1. Identify the following terms: aerobes, anaerobes, asepsis, epidemiology, microorganisms, obligatory parasite, pathogen, and sepsis.

2. Describe the two main shapes of bacteria and differentiate between aerobes and anaerobes.

3. Describe how some bacteria protect themselves against adverse conditions by forming capsules and spores. Also, state the problems which these cause in efforts to control microbial activity.

4. State six potential means of disease transmission in the dental office and list the three microorganisms which are of particular concern here.

5. Describe the special precautions to be taken when treating hepatitis and AIDS patients.

6. Define, and differentiate between, sterilization and disinfection.

7. Discuss the use of wiping agents for disinfecting and sterilizing purposes.

8. Demonstrate competence in: routine scrubbing of hands; preparation of instruments for sterilization by autoclaving and by dry heat.

EXERCISES

1. Bacteria which require oxygen to grow are called _____.

    (a) aerobes
    (b) anaerobes
    (c) bacilli
    (d) diplococci

2. _____ means the condition of being free from pathogenic microorganisms.

    (a) Asepsis
    (b) Disinfected
    (c) Sepsis
    (d) Sterile

3. At a temperature of 160° Centigrade, dry heat sterilization requires _____ minutes.

   (a) 60
   (b) 120
   (c) 150
   (d) 180

4. _____ is a study of the spread or the transmission of diseases.

   (a) Epidemiology
   (b) Microbiology
   (c) Pathogenicity
   (d) Sarcina

Match the following diseases and causative agents:

5. _____ Yeasts   (a) Syphilis

6. _____ Rickettsiae   (b) Tuberculosis

7. _____ Spirochetes   (c) Typhus

8. _____ Virus   (d) Measles

                             (e) Thrush

9. Prolonged exposure to _____ solution may cause a gold-brown skin discoloration.

   (a) alcohol
   (b) glutaraldehyde
   (c) household bleach
   (d) orange solvent

10. _____ is disease transmission by dirty hands or contaminated articles such as instruments, towels and drinking glasses.

   (a) Carrier
   (b) Droplet
   (c) Indirect
   (d) Operator

11. There is a vaccine available to prevent _____.

   (a) Infectious Hepatitis (Type A)
   (b) Serum Hepatitis (Type B)
   (c) Hepatitis non A/non B
   (d) None of the above

12. Because it causes the mechanical disruption of bacteria, the ultrasonic cleaner may be used to replace other means of sterilization.

    (a) true
    (b) false

Match the following terms and definitions:

13. _____ Pathogen   (a) A nonmotile obligatory parasite.

14. _____ Microorganism   (b) The forms that some bacteria take to withstand unfavorable conditions.

15. _____ Capsules   (c) Living organisms that are so small as to be visible only with a microscope.

16. _____ Spores   (d) Protective mucoid coatings on the surface of bacteria.

                              (e) Any organism capable of causing disease.

17. In the presence of water, at 15 psi and 121° Centigrade, _____ is generated.

    (a) autoclaving
    (b) disinfection
    (c) implosion
    (d) saturated steam

18. Sterile instruments may safely be stored on open tray racks and in conventional dental cabinets.

    (a) true
    (b) false

19. If the object is covered with the solution, glutaraldehyde is capable of sterilization in 10 minutes.

    (a) true
    (b) false

20. _____ is the process by which all forms of life are completely destroyed in a circumscribed area.

    (a) Boiling water
    (b) Chemical disinfection
    (c) Sterilization
    (d) Ultrasonic cleaning

21. _____ infection caused by inhaling the mist of bacteria and debris from the handpiece is a hazard to the dentist and assistant.

    (a) Droplet
    (b) Indirect
    (c) Operator
    (d) Self-

22. Most viruses can be successfully treated with antibiotics.

    (a) True
    (b) False

23. Implosion is part of the action of _____.

    (a) autoclaving
    (b) disinfection
    (c) dry heat sterilization
    (d) ultrasonic cleaning

24. A _____ is an agent which destroys within 10 minutes all vegetative bacteria except the hepatitis virus and bacterial spores.

    (a) bactericide
    (b) disinfectant
    (c) germicide
    (d) all of the above

25. _____ is one of the most common bacteria in the mouth.

    (a) Aspergillus
    (b) Lactobacillus
    (c) Sarcina
    (d) Tubercle bacillus

PROCEDURE: PREPARING INSTRUMENTS FOR STERILIZATION BY AUTOCLAVING		
GOAL: The student will demonstrate preparation of instruments for autoclaving including loading and simulated operation of the autoclave.		
SE = Student evaluation C = Criterion met IE = Instructor evaluation X = Criterion not met	SE	IE
1. **Instruments and Materials:** household rubber gloves, soiled instruments, stiff brush, liquid soap, running water, ultrasonic cleaner (optional), autoclave bag or wrap, autoclave tape.		
2. Identified types of instruments sterilized by autoclaving.		
3. Removed all soil from instruments by hand scrubbing and/or using ultrasonic cleaner.		
4. Rinsed and drained instruments thoroughly.		
5. Wrapped and sealed instruments for autoclaving.		
6. Loaded autoclave to allow proper flow of steam.		
7. Checked autoclave for proper water level and closed autoclave door.		
8. Identified time, temperature, and pressure necessary for sterilization of that load.		
Comments:		

PROCEDURE: PREPARING INSTRUMENTS FOR DRY HEAT STERILIZATION		
GOAL: The student will demonstrate preparation of instruments for dry heat sterilization.		
SE = Student evaluation C = Criterion met IE = Instructor evaluation X = Criterion not met	SE	IE
1. **Instruments and Materials:** household rubber gloves, soiled instruments, stiff brush, liquid soap, running water, ultrasonic cleaner (optional), sterilization wrap.		
2. Identified types of instruments sterilized by dry heat.		
3. Removed all soil from instruments by hand scrubbing and/or using ultrasonic cleaner.		
4. Rinsed and drained instruments thoroughly.		
5. Dried instruments thoroughly.		
6. Wrapped and sealed instruments for dry heat sterilization.		
7. Identified the time and temperature combination for this instrument load.		
Comments:		

PROCEDURE: ROUTINE SCRUBBING OF HANDS		
GOAL: The student will demonstrate accepted technique for routine scrubbing of hands.		
SE = Student evaluation C = Criterion met IE = Instructor evaluation X = Criterion not met	SE	IE
1. **Instruments and Materials:** brush, liquid soap, running water, paper towels.		
2. Wet brush and hands and applied liquid soap.		
3. Brush and lather used to scrub soiled areas. (Back of hands, palms, fingers, cuticle, and under nails.)		
4. Rinsed hands under running water until soap removed.		
5. Dried surfaces of hands with clean paper towel.		
6. Used soiled paper towel to turn off water faucets.		
7. Discarded towel to prevent spread of contamination.		
Comments:		

CHAPTER 7   ORAL PATHOLOGY

LEARNING GOALS

The student will be able to:

1. Describe body defenses and identify, by matching, the related terminology.

2. List the four major signs of inflammation and describe how inflammation helps to protect the body.

3. Describe the classifications of common lesions using the proper terminology.

4. Identify, by matching, diseases of the teeth, dental pulp, and oral soft tissues.

5. List the three major symptoms which could mean oral cancer and identify the following terms associated with it: neoplasm, benign tumor, malignant tumor, squamous cell carcinoma, adenocarcinoma.

7. Identify, by matching, secondary oral disorders.

EXERCISES:

1. A periapical abscess may drain into the mouth through a _____.

   (a) cyst
   (b) fistula
   (c) granuloma
   (d) periodontosis

2. An ulcer is a _____.

   (a) lesion extending below the surface.
   (b) lesion above the surface.
   (c) lesion that is flat or even with the surface.
   (d) lesion that may be either raised or flat.

3. A hematoma is a _____.

   (a) lesion extending below the surface.
   (b) lesion above the surface.
   (c) lesion that is flat or even with the surface.
   (d) lesion that may be either raised or flat.

4. _____ is a fusion of cementum or dentin with the alveolar bone due to absence of the periodontium.

   (a) Ankylosis
   (b) Fluorosis
   (c) Hypoplasia
   (d) Impaction

5. _____ is a chronic degenerative disease characterized by bone loss, migration and loosening of the teeth in the absence of inflammation.

   (a) Dehiscence
   (b) Glossitis
   (c) Periodontitis
   (d) Periodontosis

6. A thin grayish-white pseudomembrane is typical of _____.

   (a) acute necrotizing ulcerative gingivitis
   (b) leukoplakia
   (c) measles
   (d) trismus

7. _____ is commonly referred to as a "cold sore" or "fever blister."

   (a) Aphthous Ulcer
   (b) Cellulitis
   (c) Herpes Simplex, Type 1
   (d) Herpes Simplex, Type 2

Match the following terms and definitions:

8. _____ Pulpalgia

9. _____ Pulpitis

10. _____ Pulp polyp

(a) A localized inflammation at the radical tip of the tooth.

(b) A large bulbous mass in the dental pulp.

(c) Pain in the dental pulp.

(d) Inflammation of the dental pulp.

11. _____ are substances on the surface of the microbial cells which initiate the immune response within the body.

    (a) Antibodies
    (b) Antigens
    (c) Histamines
    (d) Macrophages

12. Which of the following is/are major signs of inflammation?

    (a) heat
    (b) pain
    (c) redness
    (d) swelling (edema)
    (e) all of the above

13. _____ is neuralgia of the trigeminal nerve and has been described as excruciating, stabbing and searing pain.

    (a) Bruxism
    (b) Fibroma
    (c) Mandibular neoplasia
    (d) Tic douloureux

14. Unusual bleeding or discharge, a lump or swelling or a sore that does not heal within two weeks may be symptoms of _____.

    (a) cheilitis
    (b) oral cancer
    (c) rubella
    (d) xerostomia

15. _____ usually begins as redness and peeling of the skin at the angles of the mouth. As the condition continues, cracks occur in the skin and mucous membranes at the commissure of the lips.

    (a) Cellulitis
    (b) Cheilosis
    (c) Leukoplakia
    (d) Tetanus

16. _____ is an allergic reaction that may be severe enough to cause death.

    (a) Anaphylaxis
    (b) Antihistamine
    (c) Histamine
    (d) Urticaria

17. _____ is a personality disorder manifested by extreme aversion to food.

   (a) Adenocarcinoma
   (b) Anorexia nervosa
   (c) Tetanus
   (d) Tic douloureux

18. _____ is a disease initiated by microbial activity involving the hard portions of the teeth which are exposed in the oral cavity.

   (a) Ankylosis
   (b) Cementoclasia
   (c) Dental caries
   (d) Dental Fluorosis

19. _____ is an inflammatory process occurring in a gingival "flap" of tissue found over a partially erupted tooth.

   (a) Gingivitis
   (b) Pericoronitis
   (c) Periodontal abscess
   (d) Periodontal pocket

20. Candida albicans causes the oral infection known as _____.

   (a) dehiscence
   (b) fluorosis
   (c) hyperemia
   (d) moniliasis

21. _____ is an inflammation that is not controlled and contained within a localized area but instead spreads throughout the substance of the tissue or organ.

   (a) Cellulitis
   (b) Cheilosis
   (c) Gingivitis
   (d) Periodontitis

22. _____ is of particular concern to the dental assistant because of the danger of infection through a puncture wound from a soiled instrument.

   (a) Bulimia
   (b) Leukemia
   (c) Syphilis
   (d) Tetanus

Match the following terms and definitions:

23. _____ Abrasion

24. _____ Attrition

25. _____ Erosion

(a) Physiological wear as the result of natural mastication.

(b) Superficial loss of dental hard tissue by a chemical process that does not involve bacteria.

(c) An abnormal pattern of resorption of unknown origin.

(d) Pathologic wearing away of dental hard tissue by the friction of a foreign body.

CHAPTER 8   PHARMACOLOGY AND PAIN CONTROL

LEARNING GOALS

The student will be able to:

1. Identify, by schedule, the major drugs covered by the Controlled Substances Act.

2. Identify the major routes of drug administration.

3. Describe the three types of drugs used in dentistry for the control of anxiety.

4. Differentiate between mild analgesics and strong analgesics, i.e., narcotics and synthetic narcotics.

5. Describe the specialized uses and hazards (in dentistry) of the antibiotics: penicillin, tetracycline, and erythromycin.

6. Describe the uses of vasoconstrictors, antihistamine drugs, corticosteroids, atropine sulfate, oxygen and hemostatics.

7. Describe obtaining local anesthesia by block and by infiltration injection techniques.

8. Identify the four stages of general anesthesia and describe the agents most commonly used to produce general anesthesia.

9. Describe the use of nitrous oxide-oxyen relative analgesia in dentistry and identify the three planes of analgesia.

10. When told which tooth or area is to be anesthetized, demonstrate competence in placing topical anesthetic prior to an injection of local anesthesia.

11. Demonstrate competence is preparing a local anesthetic syringe.

EXERCISES

1. A prescription for a Schedule III or a Schedule IV drug may not be refilled more than _____ months after the date of prescribing.

   (a) 3
   (b) 4
   (c) 6
   (d) 12

2. The dental assistant may give medication to the patient if samples are available in the office.

    (a) true
    (b) false

3. During the last trimester of pregnancy, infancy and early childhood, the antibiotic _____ may produce permanent discoloration of the teeth and possible enamel hypoplasia.

    (a) cephalosporin
    (b) erythromycin
    (c) penicillin
    (d) tetracycline

4. In nitrous oxide-oxygen relative analgesia, if the patient moves beyond the second plane of relative analgesia, _____ oxygen will help return the patient to the desired plane.

    (a) decreased
    (b) increased

5. Dilaudid is a synthetic narcotic and therefore does not come under the Controlled Substances Act.

    (a) true
    (b) false

Match the following routes for administration of drugs:

 6. _____ intravenously   (a) by injection

 7. _____ orally   (b) by placement under the tongue

 8. _____ parenterally   (c) by mouth

 9. _____ subcutaneously   (d) by injection into the muscle

10. _____ sublingually   (e) by injection into the vein

                               (f) by injection under the skin

11. In dentistry, Librium and Valium are used for the control of
_____.

    (a) anxiety
    (b) hypnotics
    (c) pain
    (d) sedation

12. A/an _____ is a substance placed in an anesthetic compound to
retain the anesthetic solution in the tissues for a longer
period of time.

    (a) amide
    (b) ester
    (c) paresthesia
    (d) vasoconstrictor

13. _____ anesthesia is administered by injecting the anesthetic
solution in the proximity of the nerve trunk.

    (a) Block
    (b) Infiltration
    (c) Intraosseous
    (d) Periodontal ligament

14. The _____ on the anesthetic syringe makes it possible to
aspirate to be certain that the needle has not entered a blood
vessel.

    (a) barrel
    (b) harpoon
    (c) hub
    (d) piston rod

15. _____ is the stage of surgical anesthesia in which the patient
may become uncooperative and nauseous.

    (a) Stage 1
    (b) Stage 2
    (c) Stage 3
    (d) Stage 4

16. _____ may be administered to check the secretion of saliva and
mucus during anesthesia for dental procedures.

    (a) Atropine sulfate
    (b) Demerol
    (c) Enflurane
    (d) Vasoconstrictors

17. _____ drugs have some medical use and a high abuse potential with severe psychic and physical dependence.

    (a) Schedule   I
    (b) Schedule   II
    (c) Schedule III
    (d) Schedule   IV

Match the following drug terminology and definitions:

18. _____ Idiosyncrasy

19. _____ Side effect

20. _____ Drug interaction

(a) An unavoidable effect that results from administration of an average dose of a drug.

(b) A drug dose that causes death.

(c) An unsuspected, abnormal response to a drug, such as central nervous system stimulation by a barbiturate.

(d) A response resulting from two or more drugs or other therapeutic measures acting simultaneously.

21. _____ is a vasoconstrictor.

    (a) Bacitracin
    (b) Epinephrine
    (c) Morphine sulfate
    (d) Secobarbital

22. _____ is/are used to arrest the flow of blood.

    (a) Antibiotics
    (b) Atropine sulfate
    (c) Corticosteriods
    (d) Hemostatics

23. Pentothal and Brevital are general anesthetics which are administered _____.

    (a) by inhalation
    (b) intravenously
    (c) orally
    (d) sublingually

24. Percodan is a _____ drug.

    (a) Schedule   I
    (b) Schedule II
    (c) Schedule III
    (d) Schedule IV

25. The Latin abbreviation "b.i.d." means _____.

    (a) before meals
    (b) between meals
    (c) take at bedtime
    (d) twice daily

PROCEDURE: APPLICATION OF TOPICAL ANESTHESIA		
GOAL: The student will demonstrate the application of topical anesthesia in preparation for injection of local anesthesia for the maxillary left central incisor.		
Note: This is an entry level skill. The student should learn how to apply topical anesthesia for any local anesthesia injection.		
SE = Student evaluation C = Criterion met IE = Instructor evaluation X = Criterion not met	SE	IE
1. **Instruments and Materials:** cotton-tipped applicator, topical anesthetic ointment or liquid to simulate topical ointment, sterile gauze sponge.		
2. Washed hands.		
3. Explained procedure to patient.		
4. Placed topical anesthetic on cotton-tipped applicator and replaced cover on the ointment container.		
5. Used a sterile gauze sponge to gently dry the correct injection site.		
6. Removed the gauze sponge and positioned the applicator with the ointment directly on the injection site.		
7. Left the applicator in place for 2 to 5 minutes.		
Comments:		

PROCEDURE: PREPARATION OF A LOCAL ANESTHETIC SYRINGE		
GOAL: The student will demonstrate sterile technique for the preparation of a local anesthetic syringe for infiltration anesthesia using an aspirating syringe and local anesthetic cartridge with the epinephrine ratio as specified by the dentist (or instructor).		
SE = Student evaluation C = Criterion met IE = Instructor evaluation X = Criterion not met	SE	IE
1. Instruments and Materials: appropriate type of syringe, needle length and type of anesthetic cartridge, gauze sponges and disinfecting solution		
2. Washed hands.		
3. Disinfected needle end of anesthetic cartridge.		
4. Placed cartridge on syringe and engaged harpoon.		
5. Opened disposable needle packet without touching or contaminating the needle.		
6. Attached the needle to the syringe.		
7. Loosened the needle guard, but left it on the needle.		
Comments:		

LEARNING GOALS

The student will be able to:

1. Identify the following terms: force (tensile, compressive, shearing), stress (tensile, compressive, shearing), strain, elasticity, elastic limit, modulus of elasticity, and ultimate strength.

2. Differentiate between ductility and malleability and identify the following: flow, hardness, relaxation and distortion.

3. Describe thermal conductivity and thermal expansion and state why they are important in dentistry.

4. Discuss adhesion in terms of: viscosity, contact angle, wetting, film thickness, and surface tension. State why these are of concern in dentistry.

5. Identify the following terms: hydrocolloid, sol, gel, reversible hydrocolloids, irreversible hydrocolloids and gelation temperature.

6. Compare dental impression materials in terms of their composition, characteristics, and uses in dentistry.

7. Describe how powdered dental stone and plaster are reformed into solid gypsum including: comparative water/powder ratio, setting time, setting expansion, and the factors affecting final strength.

8. Identify the following terms relating to syntheic resins: polymer, monomer, polymerization, self-cured, heat-cured and light-cured.

9. Discuss restorative resins in terms of composition and characteristics.

10. Describe acid etch technique and bonding.

11. Identify the following terms relating to metals in dentistry: alloys, amalgam, cast structure, wrought structure, soldering, flux, and welding.

12. Describe the primary purpose of each component of amalgam alloy. Also identify the importance of the role of each of the following in dental amalgam: mercury/alloy ratio and setting reaction.

13. Describe the hazards of incorrect handling of mercury and discuss the mercury hygiene recommendations listed in the text.

14. Compare the most commonly used dental cements and cavity liners in terms of composition, characteristics and uses in dentistry.

15. Describe and state the primary uses of the following dental waxes: inlay, baseplate, sticky, boxing and utility.

EXERCISES

Match the following terms and definitions:

1. _____ Force

(a) The ability of a body to resume its original shape when the external force is removed.

2. _____ Strain

(b) Any push or pull upon matter.

3. _____ Stress

(c) The distortion or change produced in a body as the result of its internal reaction to an external force.

(d) The internal reaction to an externally applied force.

4. _____ is the characteristic of a liquid to flow easily over the surface.

(a) Adhesion
(b) Film thickness
(c) Viscosity
(d) Wetting

5. Resin is changed from its plastic, and easily molded shape, into a hardened one by a process called _____.

(a) adhesion
(b) investment
(c) polymerization
(d) rheology

6. Tooth structure has a _____ rate of thermal conductivity.

   (a) high
   (b) low

7. In dental _____, the powder particles contain crystals that are spongy and irregular in shape.

   (a) model plaster
   (b) stone

8. _____ is the retarder added to alginate impression material to slow the set.

   (a) Calcium sulfate
   (b) Potassium alginate
   (c) Potassium fluoride
   (d) Trisodium phosphate

9. Agar impression materials are examples of _____ hydrocolloids.

   (a) irreversible
   (b) reversible

Match the following terms and definitions:

10. _____ Gel

11. _____ Hydrocolloid

12. _____ Sol

   (a) A colloid in which the dispersing medium is water.

   (b) Liquid colloid.

   (c) Suspension of particles in some type of dispersing medium.

   (d) Semisolid colloid.

13. In _____ resins, a/an _____ is placed in the monomer to bring about curing.

   (a) self-cured   polymer
   (b) heat-cured   accelerator
   (c) light-cured   initiator
   (d) self-cured   visible light

14. _____ cement is a good thermal insulator, has a crushing strength of 2,500 psi, and may be one of the least irritating of any of the dental cements.

    (a) Polycarboxylate
    (b) Resin
    (c) Silicate
    (d) Zinc oxide-eugenol

15. _____ are contraindicated for use under resins and composites.

    (a) Calcium hydroxide
    (b) Cavity liners
    (c) Cavity varnishes
    (d) A and C

16. _____ is poisonous, is liquid at room temperature and increased heat causes it to change to vapor.

    (a) Alloy
    (b) EBA
    (c) Mercury
    (d) ZOE

17. _____ is the process by which the mercury and alloy are mixed together in order to form the "plastic" mass of amalgam used to create the dental restoration.

    (a) Amalgamator
    (b) Minimal mercury technique
    (c) Polymerization
    (d) Trituration

Match the following terms and defintions:

18. _____ Ductility

    (a) The ability of a material to withstand permanent deformation under tensile stress without fracture.

19. _____ Malleability

    (b) The ability of a material to withstand permanent deformation under compressive stress without rupture.

    (c) The ability of a material to withstand permanent deformation under shearing stress without rupture.

20. _____ cement is stronger than zinc oxide-eugenol cement, but not as strong as zinc phosphate cement.

    (a) Calcium hydroxide
    (b) EBA
    (c) Polycarboxylate
    (d) Zinc silico-phosphate

21. Potassium sulfate is added to gypsum products to _____ set and to _____ expansion.

    (a) accelerate   reduce
    (b) reduce   speed
    (c) retard   eliminate

22. Impression compound is _____.

    (a) brittle
    (b) inelastic
    (c) thermoplastic
    (d) all of the above

23. Zinc oxide impression pastes are most commonly used to take _____ impressions of wholly edentulous jaws.

    (a) corrective
    (b) preliminary
    (c) secondary
    (d) A and C

24. Amalgamation takes place when _____ is added to an alloy.

    (a) copper
    (b) mercury
    (c) tin
    (d) zinc

25. Restorations of _____ have the important characteristic that they can be highly polished.

    (a) blended composites
    (b) self-cured composites
    (c) self-cured microfilled
    (d) unfilled

26. The acid etch technique utilizes a solution of 35 to 50 percent of _____ acid.

    (a) BIS-GMA
    (b) ethylene dimethacrylate
    (c) methacrylate
    (d) phosphoric

27. If _____ is severe, the pulp is continually irritated, and may cause the tooth to remain sensitive following placement of the restoration.

    (a) acidity
    (b) galvanic action
    (c) mastication
    (d) microleakage

28. _____ impression materials are used primarily in restorative dentistry for quadrant inlay and crown and bridge impressions.

    (a) Alginate
    (b) Elastomeric
    (c) Gypsum
    (d) Wax

29. The _____ the water/powder ratio, which reflects more powder and less water, the greater the setting expansion and strength.

    (a) higher
    (b) lower

30. Polymerization takes place in pit and fissure sealants as the result of _____.

    (a) heat-curing
    (b) light-curing
    (c) self-curing
    (d) B or C

31. The acid etch technique and composite resins are used together in _____.

    (a) annealing
    (b) autopolymerization
    (c) bonding
    (d) trituration

32. _____ is the main component of amalgam alloy and it imparts a high luster.

    (a) copper
    (b) silver
    (c) tin
    (d) zinc

33. _____ wax is used for holding artificial denture wax-ups.

    (a) Baseplate
    (b) Boxing
    (c) Sticky
    (d) Utility

34. Most acrylic dentures are fabricated from _____ denture base materials used in the powder-liquid form.

    (a) cold-cured
    (b) heat-cured
    (c) light-cured
    (d) self-cured

35. _____ investment materials are used in the process of making cast metal restorations such as inlays and crowns.

    (a) Alginate
    (b) Compound
    (c) Gypsum-bonded
    (d) Synthetic resin

LEARNING GOALS

The student will be able to:

1. Identify the key nutrients and describe their primary functions.

2. Discuss the role of carbohydrates in nutrition and differentiate between monosaccharides, disaccharides and polysaccharides.

3. Describe the role of fats in the diet and identify three types of fatty acids and their sources.

4. State the role of protein in the diet and identify the terms: complete protein, incomplete protein and essential amino acids.

5. Identify essential vitamins and minerals by stating their primary function and listing one good source of each.

6. State why foods are divided into the four major food groups, identify foods found in each group, and note the primary nutritional contributions of each group. Also, identify empty calories in terms of the foods containing them.

7. Describe the role of nutrition in dental caries.

8. Identify, by matching terms and definitions, the oral manifestations of nutritional disorders.

9. Demonstrate competence in planning a special diet for a patient with an injured anterior tooth.

10. Demonstrate competence in dietary evaluation and counseling.

EXERCISES

1. _____ is the process by which an individual utilizes food to meet bodily needs.

   (a) Diet
   (b) Digestion
   (c) Nutrition
   (d) Metabolism

2. _____ is the form of sugar normally found in the blood. It is utilized by the tissues as a source of energy.

   (a) Fructose
   (b) Glucose
   (c) Lactose
   (d) Sucrose

3. Olive oil is a source of _____ fatty acids.

   (a) fully saturated
   (b) monounsaturated
   (c) polyunsaturated
   (d) B and C

4. Iodine is an essential _____, and its deficiency in the body causes _____.

   (a) amino acid   anemia
   (b) mineral   goiter
   (c) protein   diabetes
   (d) vitamin   rickets

5. Vitamin _____ is essential in healing. The tendency to bruise easily is one symptom of a deficiency of this vitamin.

   (a) A
   (b) C
   (c) D
   (d) E

6. _____ are the only nutrient that can make new cells and rebuild body tissues.

   (a) Carbohydrates
   (b) Fats
   (c) Minerals
   (d) Proteins

7. Liver, organ meats, whole-grain produce, and green leafy vegetables are good sources of the mineral _____.

   (a) chromium
   (b) copper
   (c) iron
   (d) phosphorus

8. Carbohydrates must be broken down into the form of a _____ before they can be utilized by the body.

   (a) disaccharide
   (b) monosaccharide
   (c) polysaccharide
   (d) saturated saccharide

9. _____ vitamins are not easily lost in cooking and can be stored in the body. Vitamin _____ is an example of this type.

   (a) B-complex B_{12}
   (b) Fat-soluble   C
   (c) Fat-soluble   D
   (d) Water-soluble   K

10. _____ is a complex fat-related compound found in practically all body tissues. Elevated serum levels are related to cardiac disease.

   (a) Amino acid
   (b) Cholesterol
   (c) Phenylalanine
   (d) Tryptophan

11. All 22 different amino acids are ordinarily required for the _____ of tissue proteins.

   (a) anabolism
   (b) catabolism
   (c) metabolism
   (d) synthesis

12. The oral manifestations of _____ may be a burning sensation, numbness or a smooth, bright-red appearance of the tip and margins of the tongue.

   (a) pellagra
   (b) pernicious anemia
   (c) rickets
   (d) scurvy

13. <u>Streptococcus</u> <u>mutans</u> begins the breakdown of enamel in dental caries by converting _____ into lactic and pyruvic acids.

    (a) amino acids
    (b) coenzymes
    (c) proteins
    (d) sugars

14. One cup of peach ice cream contains _____ teaspoons of sugar.

    (a) 5
    (b) 11
    (c) 15
    (d) 19

15. _____ is a trace mineral that is important in the formation of hemoglobin.

    (a) Copper
    (b) Fluorine
    (c) Iron
    (d) Zinc

16. A deficiency of the vitamin _____ may cause pellagra, glossitis, digestive and mental disorders.

    (a) folic acid
    (b) niacin
    (c) riboflavin
    (d) thiamine

17. _____ increase the amount of cholesterol in the blood and are not an essential part of the diet.

    (a) Linoleic acids
    (b) Monounsaturated fats
    (c) Polyunsaturated fats
    (d) Saturated fats

18. _____ is/are essential in the preservation of the body fluid balance and renal compensatory mechanisms.

    (a) Coenzymes
    (b) Complete amino acids
    (c) Vitamin D
    (d) Water

19. The _____ food group is an important source of calcium, protein and other nutrients.

    (a) bread and cereal
    (b) meat
    (c) milk
    (d) vegetable and fruit

20. _____ is the result of a severe vitamin C deficiency.

    (a) Angular cheilosis
    (b) Glossitis
    (c) Paresthesia
    (d) Scurvy

21. A patient on a soft diet should avoid _____.

    (a) asparagus tips
    (b) fruit juice
    (c) poached eggs
    (d) potato chips

22. _____ is the term used to describe cracks and fissures at the corners of the mouth.

    (a) Angular cheilosis
    (b) Ariboflavinosis
    (c) Glossitis
    (d) Glossopyrosis

23. From the meat group _____ daily serving(s) are recommended for the average adult.

    (a) 1 large
    (b) 2 or more small
    (c) 4 small
    (d) A or C

24. The orthodontic patient should avoid _____.

    (a) fried eggs
    (b) milk shakes
    (c) popcorn
    (d) sliced apples

25. _____ is a nutritional disorder characterized by dermatitis, diarrhea, depression and death.

    (a) Anemia
    (b) Ariboflavinosis
    (c) Pellagra
    (d) Scurvy

PROCEDURE: PLANNING A SPECIAL DIET (FOR A PATIENT WITH INJURED ANTERIOR TEETH)		
GOAL: The student will prepare a written plan for a well-balanced soft diet for two days using herself as the patient.		
SE = Student evaluation C = Criterion met IE = Instructor evaluation X = Criterion not met	SE	IE
1. Diet plan contained only foods acceptable as part of a soft diet.		
2. Diet plan for each day included food from all four food groups in the quantities appropriate for the nutrition of the patient.		
3. The diet plans did not include excessive empty calories or food high in sugar content.		
4. The diet plans were practical to follow and included varied foods that were appealing to the patient.		
Comments:		

PROCEDURE: DIETARY EVALUATION AND COUNSELING		
GOAL: The student will demonstrate all steps in dietary evaluation and dietary counseling.		
SE = Student evaluation C = Criterion met IE = Instructor evaluation X = Criterion not met	SE	IE
1. Gathered information concerning patient's diet. (Prepared form, motivated client, received information needed to perform an evaluation)		
2. Evaluated information from diet diary in terms of food groups and identified problem areas. (Prepared form, transcribed information, evaluated information, identified problems)		
3. Counseled patient on how to improve diet in terms that the patient could understand.		
4. Made recommendations for improvement in keeping with the individual needs and background of the patient.		
5. Presented recommendations in such a way that the patient was most likely to accept and follow.		
Comments:		

CHAPTER 11   PREVENTIVE DENTISTRY

LEARNING GOALS

The student will be able to:

1. Identify the need for preventive dentistry and discuss the cost of dental neglect. Also, discuss the role of the dental specialties and list the major aspects of preventive dentistry.

2. Identify the role of fluorides in preventive dentistry applied through drinking water, dietary supplements, topical applications, toothpaste and fluoride rinses.

3. Describe the components of plaque, its formation and patterns of accumulation on the teeth.

4. Identify the following according to their role in preventive dentistry: the Snyder test, phase contrast microscopy, disclosing agents and personal oral hygiene.

5. Demonstrate competence in personal oral hygiene using a disclosing agent, the appropriate toothbrushing technique, dental floss and other dental health aids as needed.

6. Demonstrate competence in providing plaque control instruction to a patient.

7. Demonstrate competence in providing instruction for a patient on each of the toothbrushing methods described in the text.

EXERCISES

1. _____ are organisms that can live either in the presence or absence of oxygen.

   (a) Aerobes
   (b) Anaerobes
   (c) Facultative organisms
   (d) Leukocytes

2. Fluoride deposition in dental enamel occurs primarily during the _____ stage(s).

   (a) pre-eruption
   (b) after calcification
   (c) after eruption
   (d) A and B

3. Once plaque has been thoroughly removed, it takes about _____ hours for it to form again.

   (a) 6
   (b) 12
   (c) 24
   (d) 36

4. As a precautionary measure, it is recommended that no more than _____ mg. of sodium fluoride supplements be dispensed at one time.

   (a) 100
   (b) 223
   (c) 264
   (d) 296

Match the following according to their role in preventive dentistry:

5. _____ Endodontics

(a) To maintain the child's mouth in healthy condition and prevent the development of abnormalities.

6. _____ Oral Surgery

(b) To replace missing teeth and to prevent impairment of speech, facial harmony, masticatory and digestive function.

7. _____ Pedodontics

(c) To prevent the loss of pulpally involved teeth.

8. _____ Restorative

(d) To control caries and restore damaged teeth to health, form and function.

(e) To prevent impairment of the oral structures and facial disfigurement caused by abnormalities or accident.

9. Sodium fluorescein is used to _____.

   (a) dissolve plaque.
   (b) kill the bacteria found in plaque.
   (c) stain plaque so that it can be detected.
   (d) strengthen the outer layer of the enamel.

10. _____ is applied as a gel and has been demonstrated by clinical studies to have a considerable caries-inhibiting effect in children.

    (a) Acidulated phosphate-fluoride
    (b) Monofluorophosphate
    (c) Sodium fluoride
    (d) Stannous fluoride

11. The Synder test is used to estimate the count of _____ in the mouth.

    (a) aerobic organisms
    (b) endotoxins
    (c) epithelial cells
    (d) Lactobacillus acidophilus

12. The _____ toothbrushing method is also referred to as the Sulcus Cleansing Method.

    (a) Bass
    (b) Black
    (c) Charters
    (d) Stillman

13. A/an _____ consists of a soft wooden tip that is triangular in cross section. It is an interdental cleansing aid.

    (a) Aqua Tech
    (b) bridge threader
    (c) oral irrigation device
    (d) Stim-U-Dent

14. _____ is an effective way to remove plaque from proximal tooth surfaces.

    (a) Dental floss
    (b) Mouth rinse
    (c) Oral irrigation
    (d) Tooth brushing

15. The recommended concentration of fluoride in drinking water is approximately _____ part(s) per million (ppm).

    (a)   1
    (b)   10
    (c)   15
    (d) 100

16. Quantitative counts of <u>Streptococcus</u> <u>mutans</u> in dental plaque are done through the use of _____.

    (a) disclosing tablets
    (b) phase contrast microscopy
    (c) sodium fluorescein
    (d) the Synder test

17. The _____ learning occurs when the learner sits and listens, as in a lecture.

    (a) least
    (b) most

18. _____ plaque develops on tooth surfaces, restorations, appliances and dentures.

    (a) Epithelium-associated
    (b) Subgingival
    (c) Supragingival
    (d) Tooth-associated

19. _____ grows by: the addition of new bacteria, the multiplication of bacteria and the accumulation of bacterial and host products.

    (a) Acquired pellicle
    (b) Bacterial succession
    (b) Blanching
    (d) Plaque

20. _____ solutions should be stored in plastic containers.

    (a) Acidulated phosphate
    (b) Monofluorophosphate
    (c) Sodium fluoride
    (d) Stannous fluoride

21. _____ plaque contains predominantly, but not exclusively, motile, gram-negative organisms.

    (a) Acquired pellicle
    (b) Epithelium-associated
    (c) Subgingival
    (d) Supragingival

22. Mouth rinses may mask odors that are symptomatic of oral or systemic disease.

    (a) true
    (b) false

23. The _____ method of toothbrushing is especially suited for gingival massage.

    (a) Bass
    (b) Charters
    (c) Modified Stillman
    (d) Sulcus Cleansing

24. _____ is a nonbacterial structure composed of complex sugar-protein molecules which are a product of the saliva.

    (a) Acquired pellicle
    (b) Dental fluorosis
    (c) Immunoglobulin
    (d) Plaque

25. Clinical data indicates reductions in dental caries ranging from 17% to 42% with the use of dentifrices containing _____.

    (a) acidulated phosphate-fluoride.
    (b) sodium fluoride.
    (c) sodium monofluorophosphate.
    (d) stannous fluoride.

PROCEDURE: MAINTAINING PERSONAL ORAL HYGIENE		
GOAL: The student will demonstrate competence in personal oral hygiene.		
SE = Student evaluation C = Criterion met IE = Instructor evaluation X = Criterion not met	SE	IE
1. **Instruments and Materials:** disclosing agent, toothbrush, dentifrice, dental floss and other aids as needed.		
2. Disclosed plaque with disclosing agent.		
3. Teeth brushed using appropriate technique, without trauma to the gingiva.		
4. Floss and other aids used to remove remaining plaque without trauma to the gingiva.		
5. Repeated use of disclosing agent indicated that all plaque had been removed.		
Comments:		

PROCEDURE: PROVIDING PLAQUE CONTROL INSTRUCTION		
GOAL: The student will demonstrate competence in providing plaque control instruction to a patient.		
SE = Student evaluation C = Criterion met IE = Instructor evaluation X = Criterion not met	SE	IE
1. **Instruments and Materials**: disclosing agent, toothbrush, dentifrice, dental floss and other aids as needed.		
2. Selected teaching aids (mirror, models, photographs, etc.).		
3. Explained the need for good personal oral hygiene in terms the patient could understand and provided patient motivation.		
4. Explained and demonstrated the use of the materials and hygiene aids.		
5. Provided encouragement and assisted the patient in learning to use the materials and aids.		
6. Repeated step #5 until the patient showed confidence or the allotted time was up.		
7. Finished the session with praise, encouragement and instructions for practice at home.		
Comments:		

PROCEDURE: DEMONSTRATING TOOTHBRUSHING TECHNIQUES		
GOAL: The student will demonstrate the correct use of the following toothbrushing techniques: The Bass Method, The Modified Stillman Method and The Charters Method.		
SE = Student evaluation C = Criterion met IE = Instructor evaluation X = Criterion not met	SE	IE
1. **Bass Method.** Selected the appropriate type of toothbrush and demonstrated correct use of the technique.		
2. **Modified Stillman Method.** Selected the appropriate type of toothbrush and demonstrated correct use of the technique.		
3. **The Charters Method.** Selected the appropriate type of toothbrush and demonstrated correct use of the technique.		
4. Stated the unique features of each method and situations in which each might be most appropriate for patient use.		
Comments:		

LEARNING GOALS

The student will be able to:

1. Identify the terms psychotic, neurotic and normal behavior.

2. Describe the five needs as identified in Maslow's Hierarchy of Basic Motivational Needs.

3. Describe understanding patient behavior in terms of: fear, factors affecting behavior, emotional elements and patient responses.

4. Identify the following stress coping mechanisms: repression, rationalization, procrastination, deployment, affiliation, control of the situation and rehearsal.

5. Describe verbal and nonverbal communication and state why both are important to fully understand a message.

EXERCISES

1. _____ behavior is so severe and intense, with such deviant reactions, that social adjustment is impossible.

   (a) Hysteric
   (b) Neurotic
   (c) Normal
   (d) Psychotic

2. The _____ need follows the belongingness and love needs on the Maslow Hierarchy.

   (a) esteem
   (b) physiologic
   (c) safety
   (d) self-actualization

3. Children first acquire many of their fears from _____.

   (a) experience
   (b) other children
   (c) parents
   (d) B and C

4. The patient's response to the dental situation results primarily from causes which _____ part of the present situation.

   (a) are
   (b) are not

5. _____ is any factor that causes physical or emotional tension.

   (a) Fear
   (b) Neurotic behavior
   (c) Pain
   (d) Stress

Match the following terms and definitions:

6. _____ Repression

7. _____ Procrastination

8. _____ Deployment

9. _____ Rehearsal

(a) The turning of attention away from an unpleasant stimulus to one which is not as tension-producing.

(b) The process of making up plausible excuses or reasons for implausible behavior.

(c) The temporary unconscious forgetting of things that produce tension and/or pain.

(d) The process of avoiding a frustrating or upsetting situation by postponing facing the problem for as long as possible.

(e) The act of mentally going through a situation before it actually occurs.

10. _____ communication is perceived at an almost subconscious level.

   (a) Nonverbal
   (b) Verbal

11. According to Mehrabian's formula, _____ percent of the message is made up of facial expression and body language.

   (a) 7
   (b) 39
   (c) 46
   (d) 55

12. When a message is conveyed by _____ communication it may be invested with more emotion than otherwise would be involved.

   (a) nonverbal
   (b) verbal

13. Hysteria is a form of _____ behavior.

   (a) neurotic
   (b) psychotic
   (c) self-actualizing
   (d) socially adjusted

14. A _____ patient is likely to react to pain, but not show excessive fear or anxiety.

   (a) depressed
   (b) hypochondriac
   (c) neurotic
   (d) normal

15. The loss of teeth carries the threat of aging, bodily injury and loss of power.

   (a) true
   (b) false

16. Defense mechanisms become _____ only when they interfere with action that could avoid danger.

   (a) neurotic
   (b) phobic
   (c) physiologic
   (d) psychotic

17. It has been estimated that _____ of all spoken words are never heard.

    (a) 25%
    (b) 55%
    (c) 87%
    (d) 99%

18. People at the _____ level on Maslow's Hierarchy make full use of their talents and potential, and in so doing achieve a high level of maturation and psychological health.

    (a) belongingness needs
    (b) esteem needs
    (c) physiologic needs
    (d) self-actualizing

19. Defense mechanisms are form of _____ behavior.

    (a) coping
    (b) neurotic
    (c) psychotic
    (d) regressive

20. Any message is made up of two parts -- the statement proper and the explanation. The statement is sent _____ and the explanation is sent _____.

    (a) nonverbally   verbally
    (b) verbally   nonverbally

21. A _____ is sensitive to what the patient is expressing in terms of feelings and needs.

    (a) nonverbal communicator
    (b) procrastinator
    (c) responsive listener
    (d) schizophrenic

22. When people feel threatened, they prefer to be alone.

    (a) true
    (b) false

23. The _____ is/are particularly expressive of emotion and the
    patient's mental state of well-being.

    (a) eyes
    (b) hands
    (c) mouth
    (d) posture

24. Studies have shown that at least _____ of our communication with
    others is carried out on a nonverbal level.

    (a) 7%
    (b) 55%
    (c) 70%
    (d) 90%

25. The need to be free of anxiety, chaos and the threat of the
    unknown is a/an _____ need.

    (a) esteem
    (b) physiologic
    (c) safety
    (d) self-actualization

LEARNING GOALS

The student will be able to:

1. Describe the techniques used to help the fearful dental patient.

2. Describe the child's development through infancy, early childhood, pre-school age and grade school age. Also differentiate between chronological age, mental age and emotional age.

3. Discuss the special dental needs of the pregnant and nursing mother.

4. Identify at least three special dental problems faced by the geriatric patient.

5. Explain how educable, trainable, custodial or totally dependent mentally retarded differ in their mental and social development and describe their specialized needs for dental care.

6. Describe Down's syndrome and list at least three of the most common characteristics of these individuals.

7. Identify some of the problems faced by children born with a cleft palate or cerebral palsy.

8. Describe the special dental needs of patients with diabetes mellitus, epilepsy, muscular dystrophy, rheumatoid arthritis, cardiovascular disorders and cerebrovascular accidents.

EXERCISES

1. A child's _____ age refers to his level of intellectual capacity and development.

   (a) chronological
   (b) emotional
   (c) mental
   (d) physical

2. The trainable mentally retarded rarely exceed a/an _____ in mental age.

   (a) two-year-old
   (b) four-year-old
   (c) eight-year-old
   (d) ten-year-old

3. The patient with Down's syndrome may have dental abnormalities such as small peg-shaped teeth, forward position of the mandible and a large, fissured tongue.

   (a) true
   (b) false

4. The fear of a dental _____ is so great that he is seldom, if ever, seen in a dental office.

   (a) hypochondriac
   (b) neurotic
   (c) phobic
   (d) psychotic

5. A pregnant dental patient suffering from _____ syndrome is turned on her left side or made to sit up.

   (a) fetal drug effects
   (b) parturition
   (c) supine hypotensive
   (d) syncope

6. The childhood stage from ages _____ has been described as the "out-of-bounds" age.

   (a) birth to two years
   (b) two to four years
   (c) four to six years
   (d) six to twelve years

7. Which of the following is/are considered to be normal effects of aging found on the oral tissues?

   (a) darkening of tooth color
   (b) decreased tissue elasticity
   (c) resorption of alveolar bone and osteoporosis
   (d) loss of stippling in the gingiva
   (e) all of the above

8. A child with _____ may show signs of hyperactivity, distractability and perceptual difficulty.

   (a) learning disabilities
   (b) minimal brain injury
   (c) neurologic impairment
   (d) all of the above

9. Noise trauma, such as extensive exposure to the high-pitched whine of the dental drill, can cause _____.

   (a) conductive hearing loss
   (b) presbycusis
   (c) sensorineural hearing loss
   (d) tinnitus

10. Oral manifestations of _____ include: acetone breath, dehydration of oral soft tissues, and delayed healing.

    (a) diabetes
    (b) epilepsy
    (c) muscular dystrophy
    (d) Trisomy 21

11. Spasticity and athetosis are common types of _____.

    (a) arteriosclerosis
    (b) cerebral palsy
    (c) Down's syndrome
    (d) muscular dystrophy

12. _____ which is used to control epileptic seizures causes hyperplasia of the gingival tissue.

    (a) Dilantin
    (b) Dyslexia
    (c) Insulin
    (d) Ketoacidosis

13. General anesthesia _____ recommended for patients with muscular dystrophy.

    (a) is
    (b) is not

14. Patients with cardiovascular disorders may be treated with _____.

    (a) antibiotics as a preventive measure.
    (b) local anesthesia with epinephrine.
    (c) local anesthesia without epinephrine.
    (d) A and B
    (e) A and C

15. A stroke patient is usually also mentally ill and emotionally disturbed.

    (a) true
    (b) false

16. _____ is a systemic disease of unknown cause, characterized by inflammation of the joints.

    (a) Cerebral palsy
    (b) Muscular dystrophy
    (c) Presbycusis
    (d) Rheumatoid arthritis

17. _____ may be used to treat patients who are extremely fearful of dental treatment.

    (a) Densensitizing sessions
    (b) Distraction techniques
    (c) Progressive relaxation techniques
    (d) All of the above

18. A/an _____ child has all his primary teeth and is ready for his first visit to the dentist. This visit should be made before the child is in pain or requires emergency treatment.

    (a) 18-months-old
    (b) two-year-old
    (c) three-year-old
    (d) four-year-old

19. Because electromagnetic interferences can alter pacemaker performance, it may be advisable to avoid use of the ultrasonic scaler on a patient with a pacemaker.

    (a) true
    (b) false

20. A cleft palate patient may wear an appliance known as a/an _____ which blocks the opening in the palate.

    (a) obturator
    (b) oral brace
    (c) palatoscope
    (d) shunt

21. Always make certain that the wheels of the wheelchair are____
    before helping a handicapped patient to or from a wheelchair.

    (a) locked
    (b) parallel
    (c) unlocked
    (d) B and C

22. All Down's syndrome patients require dental treatment under
    general anesthesia.

    (a) true
    (b) false

23. A _____ patient may be a potential source of hepatitis.

    (a) CVA
    (b) geriatric
    (c) kidney
    (d) muscular dystrophy

24. Scolding a fearful patient will help him realize that his fears
    are foolish and unfounded.

    (a) true
    (b) false

25. Background noises are particularly distracting to a _____
    patient.

    (a) cerebral palsy
    (b) Down's syndrome
    (c) learning disabled
    (d) trainable mentally retarded

LEARNING GOALS

The student will be able to:

1. Identify the names, uses and routes of administration of the medical emergency drugs used in a dental practice.

2. Describe emergency treatment of complications of diseases such as diabetes, heart condition and epilepsy.

3. Describe the use of the Heimlich maneuver for obstruction of the airway by a foreign object.

4. Demonstrate taking and recording the patient's vital signs.

5. Demonstrate the treatment for syncope.

Note: The student and all dental personnel are expected to obtain and maintain a current certificate in CPR and basic first aid from the American Heart Association, The American Red Cross or similar agency.

EXERCISES

1. If the diabetic patient's breath smells like fruit, he is probably suffering from _____.

   (a) anaphylaxis
   (b) diabetic acidosis
   (c) insulin shock
   (d) petit mal seizure

2. The heart attack patient should be kept at rest in an upright position.

   (a) true
   (b) false

3. When obtaining a blood pressure reading the stethoscope disc is placed on the _____.

   (a) aortic artery
   (b) brachial artery
   (c) brachial vein
   (d) carotid artery

4. To determine the patient's pulse, palpate the _____ artery located at the inner wrist.

   (a) brachial
   (b) facial
   (c) radial
   (d) ulnar

5. The normal body temperature reading for the average adult is _____.

   (a) 97.6° F
   (b) 98.1° F
   (c) 98.6° F
   (d) 99.6° F

6. Atmospheric air ventilation, with approximately 21% oxygen, is delivered to a patient through the use of _____.

   (a) a mask with oxygen tank
   (b) CPR procedures
   (c) mouth-to-mouth resuscitation
   (d) the AmBU bag

7. The normal respiration rate of a relaxed adult is _____ breaths per minute.

   (a) 16 - 18
   (b) 18 - 20
   (c) 22 - 26
   (d) 24 - 28

8. _____ is used to dislodge a foreign body that is obstructing the airway.

   (a) An artificial airway
   (b) Cardiopulmonary resuscitation
   (c) The Heimlich maneuver
   (d) Mouth-to-nose artificial ventilation

9. _____ is commonly called fainting.

   (a) Anoxia
   (b) Cerebrovascular accident
   (c) Hyperventilation
   (d) Syncope

10. The preferred emergency medication for treatment of the
    conscious patient with a heart condition is to administer a
    stimulant such as epinephrine.

    (a) true
    (b) false

11. The following are signs of _____: loss of consciousness; no
    perceptible breathing, pulse or heartbeat and dilated pupils.

    (a) cardiac arrest
    (b) diabetic acidosis
    (c) epileptic seizure
    (d) postural hypotension

12. When a patient suffers pulmonary arrest _____ should be started
    immediately.

    (a) artificial ventilation
    (b) cardiopulmonary resuscitation
    (c) spirits of ammonia
    (d) B and C

13. _____ may be brought on by an altered emotional state such as
    when the patient becomes frightened.

    (a) Hyperthermia
    (b) Hyperventilation
    (c) Hypoventilation
    (d) Postural hypotension

14. The essential ABC's of _____ are: airway, breathing and
    circulation.

    (a) artificial ventilation
    (b) cardiogenic shock
    (c) cardiopulmonary resuscitation
    (d) the Heimlich maneuver

15. Placement of a compress is the accepted treatment to control
    _____.

    (a) cardiovascular accident
    (b) epileptic seizure
    (c) hemorrhage
    (d) insulin shock

16. Cardiopulmonary resuscitation procedures for the child eight years-of-age is the same as for the adult patient.

    (a) true
    (b) false

17. When providing emergency treatment for a patient who has stopped breathing, two rescuers use _____ chest compressions to _____ breath(s).

    (a) 5   1
    (b) 5   2
    (c) 10   2
    (d) 15   1
    (e) 15   2

18. The normal range of blood pressure for an adult male is the systolic pressure of 110-120 millimeters and the diastolic pressure of 65-80 millimeters of mercury.

    (a) true
    (b) false

19. _____ is/are drug(s) used to treat anaphylaxis.

    (a) Atropine
    (b) Benadryl
    (c) Epinephrine
    (d) Nitroglycerin
    (e) B and C

20. Artificial ventilation for the infant or small child may be administered through contact with his mouth and nose.

    (a) true
    (b) false

21. _____ is administered as treatment for angina pectoris.

    (a) Glucose
    (b) Morphine
    (c) Nitroglycerin
    (d) Sublingual sugar

22. Sugar may be administered to increase the level of glucose in the blood of the _____ patient.

    (a) diabetic acidosis
    (b) epileptic
    (c) hypoglycemic
    (d) hypertensive

23. Artificial airway devices are used on _____ patients.

    (a) conscious
    (b) unconscious

24. A/an _____ is the device that provides the blood pressure reading on a dial.

    (a) aneroid manometer
    (b) electric manometer
    (c) mercury manometer
    (d) sphygmomanometer

25. A fetid-foul breath odor may indicate _____.

    (a) lung or bronchial infection
    (b) diabetes mellitus
    (c) hypoglycemia
    (d) peptic ulcer

PROCEDURE: OBTAINING BLOOD PRESSURE AND VITAL SIGNS READING		
GOAL: The student will demonstrate obtaining and recording a patient's blood pressure and vital signs.		
SE = Student evaluation C = Criterion met IE = Instructor evaluation X = Criterion not met	SE	IE
1. **Instruments and Materials:** sphygmomanometer cuff with gauge, stethoscope, thermometer, patient's chart, pencil and paper.		
2. Seated patient with arm extended and supported.		
3. Placed blood pressure cuff around lower area of patient's upper arm.		
4. Placed stethoscope correctly in her ears. Placed the diaphragm of stethoscope on the patient's brachial artery.		
5. Inflated cuff and obtained systolic pressure reading.		
6. Deflated cuff and obtained diastolic pressure reading. Retained cuff on arm.		
7. Recorded reading on paper.		
8. Repeated procedure. Verified reading and recorded results on patient's chart.		
9. Checked and recorded patient's temperature, respiration and pulse rates.		
10. Noted unusual skin tone, breath odor or clinically significant signs present.		
11. Properly maintained and stored all equipment.		
Comments:		

PROCEDURE: PROVIDING EMERGENCY CARE FOR A PATIENT WITH SYNCOPE		
GOAL: The student will demonstrate emergency care for a patient in a state of syncope in the dental chair. The patient is breathing and has no visible signs of injury or distress.		
SE = Student evaluation C = Criterion met IE = Instructor evaluation X = Criterion not met	SE	IE
1. **Instruments and Materials:** first aid kit, spirits of ammonia ampule and gauze pad, oxygen unit, sterile mask, blanket.		
2. Called for help.		
3. Placed patient in supine position (head slighly lower than feet).		
4. Reassured patient as he showed signs of regaining consciousness.		
5. Patient remained unconscious. Wafted crushed ammonia ampule near nostrils.		
6. Used a finger sweep to check for a clear airway.		
7. Used a sterile mask to administer oxygen.		
8. Checked patient's vital signs.		
9. Followed emergency care directions given by the dentist.		
Comments:		

CHAPTER 15   DENTAL INSTRUMENTS

LEARNING GOALS

The student will be able to:

1. Identify and describe the parts and functions of the dental instruments included in this chapter.

2. Identify the three- and four-number instrument formulas and explain the significance of each number in the formulas.

3. Demonstrate sharpening hand cutting instruments on the electric instrument sharpener and using the Arkansas flat and mounted stones.

4. Identify the types, shapes and uses of dental rotary cutting instruments, discs and mandrels.

5. Describe and demonstrate the process of cleaning and sterilizing burs, diamond stones and points.

6. Demonstrate the maintenance of handpieces to include cleaning, sterilizing and lubrication according to the manufacturer's instructions.

EXERCISES

1. A _____ is an example of a hand carving instrument with a three number formula.

   (a) binangle enamel hatchet
   (b) gingival margin trimmer
   (c) straight enamel chisel
   (d) Wedelstaedt chisel

2. A _____ represents a four-number formula for hand cutting instruments.

   (a) condenser
   (b) discoid/cleoid
   (c) gingival margin trimmer
   (d) spoon excavator

3. A/an _____ is an instrument made of flexible steel with a very sharp point used to examine tooth surfaces.

   (a) cleoid
   (b) carver
   (c) explorer
   (d) spatula

4. The shank of a hand instrument is the tapered portion connecting
   the _____.

   (a) blade and nib
   (b) handle and blade
   (c) handle and monangle
   (d) shaft and handle

5. A/an _____ has a smooth beveled edge and is used to smooth out
   roughness at the margin of the restoration and the enamel.

   (a) burnisher
   (b) carver
   (c) condenser
   (d) enamel hatchet

6. Before use, the wheel surface of some electric instrument
   sharpeners must be treated with _____.

   (a) graphite powder
   (b) hot oil
   (c) light-weight oil
   (d) water

7. A/an _____ is used to stabilize cotton rolls and to control the
   tongue.

   (a) automaton
   (b) high volume evacuator
   (c) matrix strip holder
   (d) saliva ejector

8. A mounted Arkansas stone is used to sharpen _____.

   (a) curettes
   (b) hoes
   (c) scalers
   (d) A and C

9. Petroleum jelly may be used to lubricate the _____ handpiece.

   (a) contra-angle
   (b) gear-driven
   (c) right-angle
   (d) straight

10. A triple seal prophy angle handpiece is sterilized by _____.

    (a) autoclaving
    (b) boiling water
    (c) dry heat
    (d) hot oil

11. Abrasive strips composed of metal and _____ are used to reduce overhang or excessive bulk on metallic restorations.

    (a) cuttlefish bone
    (b) diamonds
    (c) ferrous oxide
    (d) pumice

12. A _____ is a mounting device used with a rotary disc.

    (a) chuck
    (b) friction grip
    (c) latch
    (d) mandrel

13. _____ burs are used with light pressure and operate most efficiently at high speed.

    (a) Carbide steel
    (b) Plain steel

14. A _____ may be used to hold dental film in the mouth, tissue during surgery and suture needles during suturing.

    (a) bite block
    (b) forcep
    (c) hemostat
    (d) retractor

15. Soiled carbide steel burs are cleaned with a bur brush, rinsed, placed in the ultrasonic cleaner, dried and sterilized in an autoclave.

    (a) true
    (b) false

16. A _____ stone is used for the reduction and finishing of gold castings.

    (a) black
    (b) gray
    (c) red
    (d) white

Match the names and shapes of the burs shown below:

17. _____   (a) End cutting fissure

18. _____   (b) Straight fissure (plain)

19. _____   (c) Inverted cone

20. _____   (d) Straight fissure --
                                     crosscut (dentate)

21. _____   (e) Tapered fissure (plain)

22. _____   (f) Round

                                 (g) Tapered fissure --
                                     crosscut (dentate)

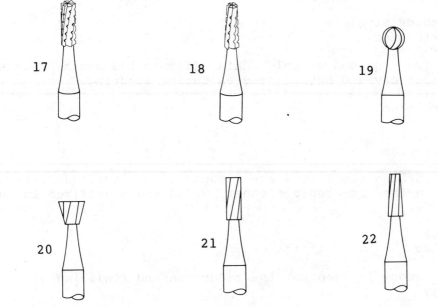

Match the names and shapes of the burs shown below:

23. _____   (a) Wheel

24. _____   (b) Inverted cone

25. _____   (c) Barrel

26. _____   (d) Round

27. _____   (e) Oval

28. _____   (f) Pointed cone

29. _____   (g) Flame

30. _____   (h) Cylinder

                     (i) Pear

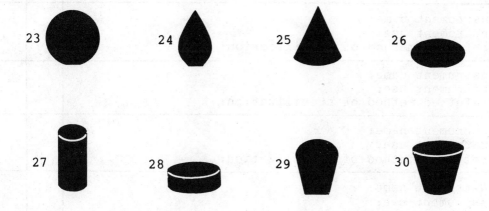

PROCEDURE: IDENTIFYING DENTAL HAND CUTTING INSTRUMENTS		
GOAL: The student will identify the name, use and method of sterilization of 10 dental hand cutting instruments (as selected by the instructor). The student may wish to review instrument sterilization methods as described in Chapter 6.		
SE = Student evaluation C = Criterion met IE = Instructor evaluation X = Criterion not met	SE	IE

1. Instrument name:
   Instrument use:
   Preferred method of sterilization:		

2. Instrument name:
   Instrument use:
   Preferred method of sterilization:		

3. Instrument name:
   Instrument use:
   Preferred method of sterilization:		

4. Instrument name:
   Instrument use:
   Preferred method of sterilization:		

5. Instrument name:
   Instrument use:
   Preferred method of sterilization:		

6. Instrument name:
   Instrument use:
   Preferred method of sterilization:		

7. Instrument name:
   Instrument use:
   Preferred method of sterilization:		

8. Instrument name:
   Instrument use:
   Preferred method of sterilization:		

9. Instrument name:
   Instrument use:
   Preferred method of sterilization:		

10. Instrument name:
    Instrument use:
    Preferred method of sterilization:		

PROCEDURE: STERILIZING CARBIDE BURS AND DIAMOND STONES		
GOAL: The student will demonstrate cleaning and sterilizing assorted carbide burs and diamond stones.		
SE = Student evaluation C = Criterion met IE = Instructor evaluation X = Criterion not met	SE	IE
1. **Instruments and Materials:** soiled carbide burs and diamond stones, bur brush, running warm water, ultrasonic cleaner and autoclave.		
2. Used the bur brush and running water to remove gross debris.		
3. Placed carbide burs and diamond stones in the ultrasonic cleaner for a minimum of three minutes.		
4. Properly wrapped carbide burs and diamond stones for autoclaving.		
5. Correctly loaded the wrapped carbide burs and diamond stones in the autoclave.		
6. Operated the autoclave at the proper time, temperature and pressure combination.		
7. Removed sterilized carbide burs and diamond stones from the autoclave and stored them properly.		
Comments:		

PROCEDURE: CLEANING, STERILIZING AND LUBRICATING HANDPIECES		
GOAL: The student will demonstrate appropriate cleaning, sterilizing and lubricating of the following handpieces: straight, contra-angle, right angle and high speed.		
SE = Student evaluation C = Criterion met IE = Instructor evaluation X = Criterion not met	SE	IE
1. **Instruments and Materials:** commercial cleaner and lubricant, disinfectant wiping agent and gauze pads, ultrasonic cleaner, autoclave, hot oil sterilizer, handpieces (straight, contra-angle, right angle and high speed).		
2. Sanitized **straight handpiece** while on the dental unit with a wiping agent and protected it until future use.		
3. Removed the **straight handpiece** from the dental unit. Prepared, cleaned and autoclaved it.		
4. Disassembled the **high speed handpiece**, cleaned, autoclaved and reassembled it.		
5. Cleaned the **contra-angle handpiece** with commercial cleaner, autoclaved, lubricated and stored it.		
6. Disassembled the **right angle handpiece.** Used commercial cleaner to clean it. Autoclaved, lubricated and reassembled it.		
Comments:		

LEARNING GOALS

The student will be able to:

1. Describe the principles of four-handed dentistry and explain how they relate to the role of the chairside assistant.

2. Describe six-handed dentistry and demonstrate the role of the coordinating assistant.

3. Identify, by matching, the classifications of motions used in four-handed and six-handed dentistry.

4. Identify and describe the function of the pieces of equipment found in the operatory, central sterilization and supply area, and in the dental laboratory.

5. Describe the routine care of the major pieces of equipment found in the dental office.

6. Describe and demonstrate the daily maintenance duties for the chairside assistant including: morning routine, between-patients routine and evening routine.

7. Demonstrate seating a dental patient in the supine and subsupine positions.

8. Demonstrate the correct seated position of the dental assistant and operator at chairside.

EXERCISES

1. The central air compressor is used to provide air _____.

   (a) for the air-driven handpieces.
   (b) for the oral evacuation system.
   (c) to raise and lower the dental chair.
   (d) B and C

2. Morning routine maintenance for the chairside assistant includes _____.

   (a) arriving 30 minutes prior to the first patient.
   (b) dusting operatory and equipment.
   (c) turning on the central air compressor.
   (d) A, B and C

Match the following terms and definitions:

3. _____ Class I motions

    (a) Motions involving movements of the arm and twisting of the body.

4. _____ Class II motions

    (b) Motions involving fingers-only movements.

5. _____ Class III motions

    (c) Motions involving movements of the fingers, wrist and elbow.

6. _____ Class IV motions

    (d) Motions involving movements of the fingers and wrist.

    (e) Motions involving movements of the entire arm from the shoulder.

7. When admitting and dismissing a patient the dental chair is placed in a/an _____ position.

    (a) 45° angle from the floor
    (b) 90° angle from the floor
    (c) supine with foot area higher
    (d) upright and lowered with the arm raised

8. Sanitation of the tubing of the oral evacuation system is essential to _____.

    (a) alter the amount of vacuum
    (b) freshen the system
    (c) prevent odors from forming
    (d) sterilize the tubing

9. Soiled instruments and materials are removed from the operatory and taken to the _____.

    (a) central sterilization area
    (b) central storage area
    (c) dental cabinets
    (d) dental laboratory

10. In addition to the dental team at chairside, six-handed dentistry directly utilizes the services of the _____.

    (a) administrative assistant
    (b) coordinating assistant
    (c) hygienist
    (d) laboratory technician

11. The seated assistant should be positioned _____.

    (a) at a 15° angle to the operator.
    (b) at the same level as the operator.
    (c) four to five inches higher than the operator.
    (d) with her feet flat on the floor.

12. The dental operatory should be maintained after each patient by _____.

    (a) checking the position of the dental chair.
    (b) removing soiled instruments.
    (c) sanitizing the equipment and accessories.
    (d) A, B and C

13. Until it can be cleaned, a soiled tray is labeled, covered and stored in with the preset trays that are ready for use.

    (a) true
    (b) false

14. Instruments routinely used for a specific dental procedure are _____.

    (a) assembled as needed during the procedure.
    (b) obtained as needed from the operatory cabinet.
    (c) placed on a preset tray.
    (d) routinely stored in the dental laboratory.

15. _____ motion(s) are most frequently used by the dentist and chairside assistant in four-handed dentistry.

    (a) Class I, II and III
    (b) Class II only
    (c) Class III and IV
    (d) Class V

16. When the patient is seated, the operating light is turned on and
    positioned _____ .

    (a) approximately 36 inches below the patient's mouth.
    (b) at the patient's forehead.
    (c) near the patient's chin.
    (d) to illuminate the oral cavity.

17. Alcohol should be rubbed on the enamel surfaces of the dental
    unit to sanitize the surfaces and to make them shine.

    (a) true
    (b) false

18. Controls on the back of the dental chair include _____ .

    (a) adjustments for the back and foot rest.
    (b) adjustments for lowering and raising the chair.
    (c) positioning the operating light.
    (d) A and B

19. The patient is in a _____ position when the dental chair is
    tilted back so that his nose and knees are at approximately the
    same level.

    (a) reclining
    (b) subsupine
    (c) supine
    (d) A and B

20. The _____ unit is equipped with handpieces, an air/water syringe
    and a vacuum attachment.

    (a) assistant's
    (b) operator's

21. The _____ tip is disposable and is discarded after use.

    (a) air/water syringe
    (b) high-volume evacuator (HVE)
    (c) saliva ejector
    (d) B and C

22. Condensation builds up in the _____ and is removed by "bleeding" through the jet opening.

    (a) central air compressor
    (b) central vacuum compressor
    (c) cuspidor
    (d) dental x-ray unit

23. The _____ may be used to blow away small bits of debris that may cling to the inner surfaces of the dental chair.

    (a) air syringe
    (b) central compressor
    (c) oral evacuation system
    (d) vacuum cleaner

24. Limited bulk supplies of dental materials are stored in the _____.

    (a) assistant's unit
    (b) dental laboratory
    (c) operatory cabinets
    (d) sterilization area

25. The air/water syringe may be used to deliver _____.

    (a) air
    (b) air and water spray
    (c) water
    (d) A, B and C

PROCEDURE: MAINTENANCE OF THE OPERATORY BETWEEN PATIENTS		
GOAL: The student will demonstrate the proper routine for operatory care and clean-up between patients.		
SE = Student evaluation C = Criterion met IE = Instructor evaluation X = Criterion not met	SE	IE
1. **Instruments and Materials:** operatory setting, gauze sponges, disinfecting agent, supplies needed for next patient.		
2. Removed soiled instruments and materials to central sterilization area.		
3. Removed debris and smudges from the dental chair.		
4. Placed dental chair in lowest position with back upright and arm raised for patient entry.		
5. Operating stools sanitized and removed from path of entry.		
6. Sanitized dental units and surfaces with a wiping agent.		
7. Sanitized air/water syringes and handpieces with wiping agent.		
8. Removed previous patient's radiographs and removed smudges from the operating light.		
9. Sanitized x-ray unit with wiping agent. Retracted machine head toward the wall.		
10. Removed smudges and debris from sinks, cabinets, drawer pulls, light switches, walls and floor.		
11. Placed appropriate prepared tray, sterile vacuum tip, chart and radiographs for the next patient.		
Comments:		

PROCEDURE: POSITIONING PATIENT, OPERATOR AND CHAIRSIDE ASSISTANT IN FOUR-HANDED DENTISTRY		
GOAL: The student will demonstrate placing the patient in the supine position, and seating the operator and assistant in the operating zones for four-handed dentistry.		
SE = Student evaluation C = Criterion met IE = Instructor evaluation X = Criterion not met	SE	IE
1. Instruments and Materials: lounge-type dental chair, operator's and assistant's stools, patient towel, towel clip and patient.		
2. Before the patient entered, lowered the chair and placed the back in upright position with the arm raised.		
3. Patient admitted, seated, draped and asked to remove eye glasses and jewelry.		
4. Gradually reclined chair so that the patient's nose and knees were approximately level.		
5. With the operator seated at the patient's right, the patient's head in the headrest was positioned in the operator's lap.		
6. The assistant was seated at patient's left, four to five inches higher than the operator. Her thighs were parallel with the patient's arm and shoulder.		
7. The assistant's feet were placed flat on the support base of the chair and her back was flush with the chair back.		
8. Cart, instrument tray and necessary equipment were positioned at the knees and lap of the assistant.		
Comments:		

CHAPTER 17   INSTRUMENT TRANSFER AND ORAL EVACUATION

LEARNING GOALS

The student will be able to:

1. Describe the zones of the clock concept as applied to four-handed
   dentistry.

2. Demonstrate assembling, adjusting and positioning of the high
   volume evacuation (HVE) tip in each area of the mouth.

3. Demonstrate selection, placement, stabilization and removal of a
   bur in the handpiece at chairside.

4. Demonstrate the different instrument grasps and the practice of
   passing the instrument in the "position of use."

5. Demonstrate exchange of instruments and materials at chairside
   using four-handed dentistry concepts.

EXERCISES

1. Using the clock concept, the _____ zone is located between
   11-o'clock and 2-o'clock.

   (a) assistant's
   (b) operator's
   (c) static
   (d) transfer

2. The _____ is used to stabilize the operator's hand, facilitate
   use of the instrument, and avoid injury to the patient.

   (a) fulcrum
   (b) pen grasp
   (c) rear delivery
   (d) stabilizer

3. Using the _____ grasp, the instrument is held in the palm of the
   hand with all five fingers surrounding and supporting the
   instrument.

   (a) inverted pen
   (b) modified palm-thumb
   (c) palm
   (d) palm-thumb

4. When using oral evacuation in the _____ quadrant the vacuum tip
   is placed at the extreme left corner of the mouth, retracting
   the cheek in the process.

   (a) mandibular left
   (b) mandibular right
   (c) maxillary left
   (d) maxillary right

5. Using a modified pen grasp, the assistant holds the vacuum tip
   handle in her _____ fist.

   (a) left
   (b) right

6. Prior to transferring a high-speed handpiece to the operator the
   assistant _____.

   (a) adjusts the controls for the psi.
   (b) extracts sufficient length of air tubing.
   (c) turns on the high volume evacuator.
   (d) A and B

7. During oral evacuation the assistant holds the _____ in her left
   hand.

   (a) air/water syringe
   (b) bur removal tool
   (c) local anesthesia syringe
   (d) used instrument

8. In four-handed dentistry, the area of exchange(or transfer
   area) is located _____.

   (a) across the chest near the patient's chin.
   (b) behind the patient's head.
   (c) directly over the patient's mouth.
   (d) over the patient's face.

9. When the assistant picks up the next instrument from the tray,
   it is grasped _____.

   (a) firmly in the palm of her hand.
   (b) in the middle of the handle.
   (c) in the position of use.
   (d) opposite the end to be used.

10. When receiving a used instrument from the operator, the assistant takes it with _____.

    (a) the little finger of her left hand.
    (b) the thumb, index and third fingers of her left hand.
    (c) the little finger of her right hand.
    (d) the thumb, index and third fingers of her right hand.

11. With the Triad handpiece, the bur is seated by _____.

    (a) pressing it on a plastic or rubber block.
    (b) removing the chuck and sleeve.
    (c) using a bur placement tool.
    (d) B and C

12. To avoid stimulating the gag reflex on the soft palate, the HVE tip should be placed gently against the tissue.

    (a) true
    (b) false

13. Which of the following may be used for tongue and cheek retraction?

    (a) a mouth mirror
    (b) the HVE
    (c) the index finger
    (d) all of the above

14. For a lingual approach for preparation of mandibular anterior teeth, the HVE is placed _____.

    (a) in the trough formed by the lower lip and the facial surfaces of the teeth.
    (b) near the lingual surface of the teeth and is also used to retract the tongue.

15. A right-handed operator most frequently works from a _____ position with either direct or indirect vision.

    (a) 4-o'clock to 6-o'clock
    (b) 8-o'clock to 10-o'clock
    (c) 9-o'clock to 11-o'clock
    (d) 12-o'clock to 2-o'clock

16. During instrument exchange, the assistant holds the new instrument in the transfer zone _____ to the instrument in use.

    (a) at a right angle
    (b) immediately next
    (c) parallel
    (d) perpendicular

17. During the instrument exchange, the operator _____.

    (a) removes his right hand away from the mouth.
    (b) maintains the fulcrum in the mouth with his right hand.
    (c) reaches for the instrument with his left hand.
    (d) B and C

18. When passing a palm grasp instrument, the assistant holds it _____.

    (a) firmly by the handles.
    (b) securely in the palm of her right hand.
    (c) without touching the beaks or working end.
    (d) A and B

19. In four-handed dentistry, dental materials are mixed _____.

    (a) in the sterilization area.
    (b) in the transfer zone.
    (c) near the patient's chin.
    (d) on the cabinet or instrument tray.

20. When the assistant attaches the handpiece to the tubing, she _____ to check that the handpiece is properly attached.

    (a) activates the rheostat
    (b) adjusts the air pressure
    (c) retracts the cord
    (d) tugs gently on the handpiece

21. A/an _____ is an example of an instrument used in a palm-thumb grasp.

    (a) enamel chisel
    (b) explorer
    (c) extraction forceps
    (d) rubber dam forceps

22. The saliva ejector is placed on the side of the mouth _____ the side where the operator is working.

    (a) near
    (b) opposite

23. The primary goal of oral evacuation is to keep the tongue and cheek away from the field of operation and to keep water from accumulating in the patient's mouth.

    (a) true
    (b) false

24. When assisting a left-handed operator the assistant is at the _____ position.

    (a) 1-o'clock to 2-o'clock
    (b) 2-o'clock to 4-o'clock
    (c) 8-o'clock to 10-o'clock
    (d) 12-o'clock to 1-o'clock

25. After receiving a used instrument, the assistant uses her _____ to bring that instrument into position for placement on the tray.

    (a) left thumb
    (b) left index and middle fingers
    (c) right thumb
    (d) right index and middle fingers

PROCEDURE: ORAL EVACUATION		
GOAL: The student will demonstrate rinsing the area under treatment and the proper placement and use of the oral evacuation tip.		
SE = Student evaluation C = Criterion met IE = Instructor evaluation X = Criterion not met	SE	IE
1. **Materials and instruments:** dental unit, sterile vacuum tip, mouth mirror, air/water syringe, patient in supine position in dental chair, operator and assistant in seated positions.		
2. With the operator seated at the 9-o'clock to 10-o'clock position, the assistant was seated at the 1-o'clock to 2-o'clock position. Air/water syringe held in assistant's left hand.		
3. Held vacuum tip in right fist using a reverse palm grasp with the lumen of the HVE tip turned toward distal to adapt to the site of operation. Held the vacuum hose close to body.		
4. Positioned the vacuum tip for the **mandibular left quadrant.** Demonstrated rinsing and evacuation of the quadrant.		
5. Positioned the vacuum tip for the **mandibular right quadrant.** Demonstrated rinsing and evacuation of the quadrant.		
6. Positioned the vacuum tip for the **maxillary left quadrant.** Demonstrated rinsing and evacuation of the quadrant.		
7. Positioned the vacuum tip for the **maxillary right quadrant.** Demonstrated rinsing and evacuation of the quadrant.		
8. Positioned the vacuum tip for the **mandibular anteriors.** Demonstrated rinsing and evacuation of the area.		
9. Positioned the vacuum tip for the **maxillary anteriors.** Demonstrated rinsing and evacuation of the area.		

PROCEDURE: INSTRUMENT GRASPS AND EXCHANGE		
GOAL: The student will demonstrate the exchange of dental instruments and materials using the pen grasp, inverted or reverse pen grasp, palm grasp and the palm-thumb grasp. All exchanges are made following a signal from the operator.		
SE = Student evaluation C = Criterion met IE = Instructor evaluation X = Criterion not met	SE	IE
1. **Instruments and materials:** mirror, explorer, spoon excavator, interproximal knife, rubber dam forceps and a root elevator. The patient is in a supine position and the operator and assistant are seated.		
2. Simultaneously picked up a mouth mirror in her right hand and explorer in her left hand. Simultaneously passed the mirror to the operator's left hand and the explorer to the operator's right hand.		
3. **Pen grasp.** Picked up the spoon excavator in her left hand. Received the used instrument from the operator with her little finger. Passed the spoon excavator to the operator's right hand in the position of use. Returned the used instrument to the instrument tray.		
4. **Reverse pen grasp.** Picked up the interproximal knife in her left hand. Received the used instrument from the operator with her little finger. Passed the new instrument to the operator's right hand in the position of use. Returned the used instrument to the instrument tray.		
5. **Palm grasp.** Picked up the rubber dam forceps near the beaks in her left hand. Received the used instrument from the operator with her little finger. Passed the handles rubber dam forceps to the operator's right hand in the position of use. Returned the used instrument to the instrument tray.		
6. **Palm thumb grasp.** Picked up the root elevator near the shank in her left hand. Received the used instrument from the operator in her little finger. Passed the root elevator to the operator's right hand in the position of use. Returned the used instrument to the instrument tray.		

PROCEDURE: BUR PLACEMENT AND REMOVAL IN A FRICTION GRIP HANDPIECE		
GOAL: The student will demonstrate the selection, placement and removal of a bur in a friction grip high-speed handpiece at chairside as part of a four-handed dentistry procedure.		
SE = Student evaluation C = Criterion met IE = Instructor evaluation X = Criterion not met	SE	IE
1. **Instruments and Materials:** #4 or #6 round friction grip carbide burs, bur remover/seating tool, plastic bur block, high speed handpiece and friction grip contra-angle handpiece.		
2. Held the handpiece in her left hand. Used the bur removal tool, in her right hand, to remove the previous bur from the handpiece.		
3. Returned the bur removal tool to the tray and picked up the bur (#4 or #6 round) in her right hand.		
4. Placed the shank of the bur in the friction grip of the handpiece.		
5. Placed tip of bur on plastic bur block. Used firm pressure to seat bur firmly in the handpiece.		
6. Tugged on the bur to determine that it was seated securely in the handpiece.		
7. Returned the handpiece to the operator in the position of use.		
Comments:		

PROCEDURE: PLACING AND REMOVING LATCH-TYPE BURS AND STONES		
GOAL: The student will demonstrate the selection, placement and removal of a bur in a latch-type low-speed handpiece at chairside as part of a four-handed dentistry procedure.		
SE = Student evaluation C = Criterion met IE = Instructor evaluation X = Criterion not met	SE	IE
1. Instruments and Materials: low-speed latch-type handpiece, assorted latch-type burs and/or stones, gauze squares.		
2. Held the low-speed handpiece in left hand. Opened the latch and removed the used bur.		
3. Picked up the next bur in right hand.		
4. Placed the notched end of the shank of the bur into the slot of the handpiece.		
5. Closed latch and gently tugged on the bur to determine that it was seated securely in the handpiece.		
8. Returned the handpiece to the operator in the position of use.		
Comments:		

LEARNING GOALS

The student will be able to:

1. Describe the physical properties of ionizing radiation and the units to measure it. Also, determine the annual maximum permissible dosage (MPD) for the operator and for the patient who will be exposed to x-radiation.

2. List, in descending order, the types of human tissues most sensitive to x-radiation. Also, describe and demonstrate protection of the patient, operator and staff according to acceptable standards for radiation hygiene.

3. Describe the structure and function of the components of the x-ray tube and the dental x-ray machine and the functions of milliamperage, kilovoltage and exposure time as they relate to the production of diagnostic quality radiographs.

4. Describe how film type and speed rating relate to exposure time and to the production of diagnostically acceptable radiographs.

5. Identify anatomic landmarks of the human skull and dentition that apply to satisfactory production of quality radiographs.

6. Identify the various sizes of dental radiographic film and state the uses of each. Also, describe and demonstrate the application of periapical, bite-wing, occlusal, extraoral and panoramic type radiographs.

7. List and describe criteria for evaluation of diagnostic radiographs of the complete dentition: adult, primary, mixed and edentulous.

8. Demonstrate the placement, exposure, and processing of film in the application of paralleling and the bisecting angle technique.

9. Demonstrate the modifications necessary for producing radiographs of edentulous, partially edentulous and mixed dentition. Also, describe the cause and the correction of errors and artifacts on radiographs.

10. Demonstrate processing and mounting of exposed dental x-ray film using manual and automatic procedures.

EXERCISES

1. Ionizing radiation occurs when _____ of an atom is removed from orbit and becomes radical in its position.

   (a) a negatively charged electron
   (b) a positively charged electron
   (c) the kinetic energy
   (d) the low current energy

2. _____ is a heavy dense element that is able to block radiation.
   (a) Gold
   (b) Iron
   (c) Lead
   (d) Quartz

3. The milliamperage selector in the x-ray machine controls the _____.

   (a) quality of potential x-radiation.
   (b) quantity of potential x-radiation.
   (c) scatter potential of the x-radiation.
   (d) voltage of the x-radiation.

4. The kilovolt selector in the x-ray machine controls the _____ for a given exposure.

   (a) exposure time
   (b) penetrating power
   (c) primary beam
   (d) scatter radiation

5. During a radiographic exposure, the patient is instructed to _____.

   (a) close his eyes
   (b) remain motionless
   (c) take deep breaths
   (d) A and B

6. The term _____ is used to describe the blackness of a radiographic film.

   (a) contrast
   (b) definition
   (c) density
   (d) detail

7. A dental occupational worker should not receive more than _____ radiation per week.

   (a)   0.5 rem
   (b)   3 rem
   (c)   5 R
   (d) 100 mR

8. The tissues of the human body most sensitive to ionizing radiation are the _____.

   (a) blood forming cells.
   (b) cells of the embryo.
   (c) gonadal tissue.
   (d) tissues of the eye.

9. By federal regulation, the pattern of radiation at the target (the skin) of the cylindrical PID must not exceed an area of _____ inches at the opening of the cylinder.

   (a) 2.75
   (b) 3.25
   (c) 3.75
   (d) 4.25

10. The lead apron and lead thyrocervical collar should be placed to cover the patient's _____.

   (a) chest
   (b) gonads
   (c) throat
   (d) A, B and C

11. The inverse square law means that the exposure time is directly proportional to the square of the _____.

   (a) kVp
   (b) mAs
   (c) penumbra
   (d) TFD

12. To increase vertical angulation, the head of the x-ray unit is pointed _____.

   (a) downward
   (b) from left to right
   (c) from right to left
   (d) upward

13. When positioning the film packet the "tab opening side" is always placed toward the tooth being radiographed.

    (a) true
    (b) false

14. Intensifying screens are used with cassette type extraoral film to _____.

    (a) improve the ability of the film to produce a diagnostic quality radiograph.
    (b) increase the amount of radiation used.
    (c) utilize the fluorescence of the scatter radiation.
    (d) A and C

15. The _____ projection is used to radiograph the sinuses of the skull.

    (a) anteroposterior
    (b) lateral extraoral
    (c) posteroanterior
    (d) Waters

16. When manually processing films, the total fixing time is _____ at 68° F.

    (a) 5 minutes
    (b) 10 minutes
    (c) 15 minutes
    (d) 20 minutes

17. When using the bisecting angle technique to expose radiographs of the maxillary centrals and laterals, the PID is placed at approximately +40 degrees.

    (a) true
    (b) false

18. The _____ is a method for determining the relative location of objects hidden within the tissues of the oral region.

    (a) buccal object rule
    (b) gray scale
    (c) inverse square law
    (d) rule of isometry

19. When positioning the patient for radiographs of the mandibular teeth using the paralleling technique, the _____ is parallel with the floor.

    (a) long axis of the maxillary teeth
    (b) long axis of the mandibular teeth
    (c) occlusal plane of the mandibular teeth
    (d) occlusal plane of the maxillary teeth

20. A/an _____ is a lead ring placed in the head of the x-ray machine at the immediate opening of the tube head. It limits the size of the useful beam.

    (a) aperture
    (b) cathode
    (c) collimator
    (d) transformer

21. To accurately expose a film with a 16-inch PID would require _____ radiation (time) than would the same film exposed with an 8-inch PID.

    (a) less
    (b) more

22. _____ mA is the setting most commonly used for dental radiographs.

    (a) 2.5
    (b) 5
    (c) 10
    (d) 70

23. Using the paralleling technique the film must be aligned parallel with the occlusal plane of the teeth being radiographed.

    (a) true
    (b) false

24. When mounting radiographs, if the raised dot is placed outward (convex) the left side of the radiograph corresponds to the _____ side of the patient's oral cavity.

    (a) left
    (b) right

25. A film that was placed backward in the mouth, with the tab side next to the teeth being radiographed, will show _____.

   (a) a blurred image
   (b) a herringbone effect
   (c) fogging
   (d) superimposed objects

26. A structure that is radiopaque will appear _____ on the radiograph.

   (a) darker
   (b) lighter

27. The operator must stand behind a protective barrier to assure protection from _____.

   (a) scatter radiation
   (b) secondary radiation
   (c) the primary beam
   (d) A, B and C

28. The developer solution reacts chemically with the _____ of the film.

   (a) hydroquinone
   (b) potassium bromide
   (c) silver bromide salts
   (d) sodium carbonate

29. To correct a foreshortened image, _____ the vertical angulation.

   (a) increase
   (b) reduce

30. The _____ technique is used to produce extraoral radiographs of the entire dentition and related supportive structures of the lower half of the face.

   (a) bite-wing
   (b) cephalometric
   (c) panoramic
   (d) xeroradiography

PROCEDURE: PREPARING A DIAGNOSTIC RADIOGRAPHIC SERIES USING THE BISECTING ANGLE TECHNIQUE		
GOAL: Using the bisecting angle technique the student will produce a complete diagnostic quality radiographic survey (periapical and bite-wings) on a radiographic-type manikin. This exercise is to be performed in accordance with the criteria established in the text -- or as specified by the instructor. The acceptable limits for chairtime, exposure and the permissible number of retakes of radiographic projections for a complete dentition survey are to be established by the instructor.		
SE = Student evaluation C = Criterion met IE = Instructor evaluation X = Criterion not met	SE	IE
1. **Instruments and Materials:** x-ray films, radiographic accessories and alignment aids, lead apron with cervical collar, dental x-ray machine, radiographic-type manikin, and patient's chart.		
2. Determined patient's previous exposure to x-radiation and recorded data on patient's health history.		
3. Placed lead apron with cervical collar on patient. Informed patient of the radiographic procedures and advised patient to close eyes during each exposure.		
4. Positioned patient, film and PID and exposed individual maxillary films.		
5. Positioned patient, film and PID and exposed individual mandibular films.		
6. Positioned patient, film and PID and exposed prescribed bite-wing films.		
7. Films stored correctly before and after the exposure.		
8. Stood behind protective barrier during exposures.		
9. Recorded number of films and amount of exposure on patient's chart.		

PROCEDURE:	PREPARING A DIAGNOSTIC RADIOGRAPHIC SERIES USING THE PARALLELING TECHNIQUE		
GOAL:	Using the paralleling technique the student will produce a complete diagnostic quality radiographic survey (periapical and bite-wings) on a radiographic-type manikin. This exercise is to be performed in accordance with the criteria established in the text -- or as specified by the instructor. The acceptable limits for chairtime, exposure and the permissible number of retakes of radiographic projections for a complete dentition survey are to be established by the instructor.		

SE = Student evaluation C = Criterion met IE = Instructor evaluation X = Criterion not met	SE	IE
1. **Instruments and Materials:** x-ray films, radiographic accessories and alignment aids, lead apron with cervical collar, dental x-ray machine, radiographic-type manikin and patient's chart.		
2. Determined patient's previous exposure to x-radiation and recorded data on patient's health history.		
3. Placed lead apron with cervical collar on patient. Informed patient of the radiographic procedures and advised patient to close eyes during each exposure.		
4. Positioned patient, film and PID and exposed individual maxillary films.		
5. Positioned patient, film and PID and exposed individual mandibular films.		
6. Positioned patient, film and PID and exposed prescribed bite-wing films.		
7. Films stored correctly before and after the exposure.		
8. Stood behind protective barrier during exposures.		
9. Recorded number of films and amount of exposure on patient's chart.		

PROCEDURE: MANUAL DEVELOPING OF RADIOGRAPHS		
GOAL: The student will develop a series of dental radiographs that are free of darkroom errors.		
SE = Student evaluation C = Criterion met IE = Instructor evaluation X = Criterion not met	SE	IE
1. **Instruments and Materials:** darkroom facilities with workspace, safelight, tanks with developer, fixer and water, thermometer, mixing rods, timer, x-rays racks and drying rack.		
2. Turned on safelight, turned off white light, closed darkroom door.		
3. Unwrapped films and secured on film rack so that none of the films were touching. Identified films on rack.		
4. Stirred solutions, using separate mixing rods. Checked temperature of solutions.		
5. Developed films for appropriate length of time.		
6. Rinsed films briefly and transferred them to the fixer solution.		
7. Fixed solutions for appropriate length of time.		
8. Rinsed films for at least 20 minutes and placed on rack to dry.		
9. Processed films were free of darkroom errors.		
Comments:		

PROCEDURE: MOUNTING RADIOGRAPHS		
GOAL: The student will mount a complete radiographic series of the dentition. This may include: permanent, mixed, primary, partially and fully edentulous radiographs.		
SE = Student evaluation C = Criterion met IE = Instructor evaluation X = Criterion not met	SE	IE
1. **Instruments and Materials:** appropriate radiographic mount, processed radiographs, view box, envelope, pen or pencil.		
2. Placed date, patient and doctor identification information on the radiographic mount.		
3. Aligned radiographs (maxillary, mandibular and bite-wings) on view box.		
4. Placed each radiograph in the appropriate window of the radiographic mount without damaging the radiographs.		
5. Identified missing radiographs or required retakes.		
6. Blocked out any unused windows on the radiographic mount with dark paper.		
7. Placed completed radiographic series in labeled envelope for safe storage.		
Comments:		

PROCEDURE: EVALUATION OF DIAGNOSTIC QUALITY OF RADIOGRAPHY SURVEY		
GOAL: The student will evaluate the diagnostic quality of a radiographic survey of the dentition produced on a patient.		
SE = Student evaluation C = Criterion met IE = Instructor evaluation X = Criterion not met	SE	IE
1. Instruments and Materials: Identified and mounted radiographic survey, view box, radiograph evaluation form, pen or pencil.		
2. Judged the acceptability of the diagnostic quality of the density and contrast of each film.		
3. Determined that each tooth of the dentition was represented on a minimum of two separate radiographs.		
4. Determined that the long axis of each tooth of the dentition was represented without distortion.		
5. Determined that a minimum of 2 millimeters of alveolar bone beyond the apex of each tooth was represented without distortion.		
6. Identified cone cuts or other signs of diagnostically unacceptable films.		
7. Checked that the periodontium of each tooth was represented accurately.		
8. Noted that all contacts of adjacent teeth were opened and represented without overlapping.		
9. Noted that each radiograph was mounted in alignment with the anatomic landmarks.		
Comments:		

LEARNING GOALS

The student will be able to:

 1. List, and describe, the three essential elements of a complete
    diagnosis and treatment plan.

 2. Describe a clinical examination of the hard and soft tissues of
    the oral cavity, face and neck.

 3. Identify Black's classificaton of cavities and the "simple,
    compound or complex" classification of cavities.

 4. Chart a dental examination using the symbols commonly employed
    to record dental conditions and treatment.

 5. Describe the essentials of a case presentation including the
    role of the administrative assistant in making financial
    arrangements.

 6. Demonstrate obtaining maxillary and mandibular alginate
    impressions for study casts.

 7. Demonstrate obtaining a wax bite registration.

 8. Demonstrate pouring, separating and trimming maxillary and
    mandibular casts for a case presentation.

EXERCISES

 1. Before the dentist consults with the patient's physician
    regarding a medical problem, it is necessary for the patient to
    sign a "Release of Information" consent form.

    (a) true
    (b) false

 2. The water used to mix the alginate for an impression should be
    at _____° F.

    (a) 65-68°
    (b) 68-70°
    (c) 70-72°
    (d) 98.6°

3. The palpation of the pairs of lymph nodes include the preauricular, parotid, submental and _____ nodes.

   (a) carotid
   (b) jugular chain
   (c) maxillary
   (d) submandibular

4. The temporomandibular joint (TMJ) is checked for mobility of the lateral, _____ and retrusive movements.

   (a) deglutition
   (b) mastication
   (c) occlusival
   (d) protrusive

5. For patient comfort while taking a maxillary alginate impression, the assistant should _____.

   (a) be certain there is adequate material at the post dam of the tray.
   (b) instruct the patient to tilt his head forward.
   (c) tell the patient to breathe through his mouth.
   (d) B and C

6. According to Black's classification, _____ cavities involve the posterior interproximal surfaces and may undermine the occlusal surface.

   (a) Class   I
   (b) Class   II
   (c) Class   III
   (d) Class   IV

7. Abraded surfaces, involving the incisal edges and occlusal surfaces of the teeth, may be classified as _____.

   (a) Class III
   (b) Class   IV
   (c) Class   VI
   (d) Class VII

8. Which of the following is/are included in the criteria for an acceptable alginate impression of the maxillary arch?

   (a) obtain registration of the mucobuccal attachment.
   (b) registration of the mylohyoid ridge.
   (c) registration of the retromolar area.
   (d) A and B

9. Which of the following is/are included in the criteria for an acceptable alginate impression of the mandibular arch?

    (a) insure registration of the tuberosities.
    (b) provide reproduction of the mylohyoid ridge.
    (c) provide reproduction of the eminence of the genial tubercle.
    (d) B and C

10. Incipient caries causes the enamel to appear _____.

    (a) black
    (b) chalky
    (c) opaque
    (d) B and C

Match the following cavity classifications and abbreviations:

11. _____   MOD   (a) Mesio-occlusal

12. _____   F   (b) Mesiolingual

13. _____   MO   (c) Mesio-occlusodistal

14. _____   ML   (d) Facial

                              (e) Fracture

15. The normal hemoglobin for men is _____ gm. per 100 ml. of blood.

    (a) 4.6 - 5.4
    (b) 4.6 - 6.2
    (c) 12.5 - 16.5
    (d) 13.5 - 18.0

16. A level _____ treatment plan includes optimum dental care.

    (a)   I
    (b)   II
    (c)   III
    (d)   IV

The following questions are based on the dental chart shown below.

17. Tooth #17 is _____.

    (a) extruded
    (b) impacted
    (c) missing
    (d) tilted mesially

18. Tooth # _____ is missing and replaced with the pontic of a fixed
    bridge.

    (a) 14
    (b) 18
    (c) 19
    (d) 29

19. Tooth #2 has _____.

    (a) DO caries
    (b) DO gold restoration
    (c) MO caries
    (d) MO silver restoration

20. Tooth #30 is restored with a _____.

    (a) full gold crown
    (b) pontic
    (c) three-quarter crown
    (d) veneer crown

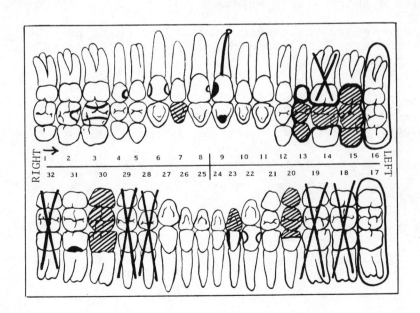

21. The anterior area of the art portion of a mandibular cast is
    _____.

    (a) cut at a 90° angle.
    (b) gently rounded.
    (c) trimmed to a 30° angle.
    (d) trimmed to a 115° angle.

22. After the treatment plan and financial arrangements have been
    accepted by the patient, the administrative assistant schedules
    him for treatment.

    (a) true
    (b) false

23. If the casts are to be mounted (articulated), a _____ is/are
    needed to show the occlusal relationship of the maxillary and
    mandibular teeth.

    (a) bilateral registration
    (b) bite registration
    (c) centric relationship
    (d) A and C

24. When the alginate impression material has set, the mandibular
    tray is removed _____.

    (a) by gently rocking it back and forth.
    (b) laterally and upward.
    (c) with a firm lifting motion.
    (d) with a sharp upward movement.

25. Each impression tray should be deep enough to provide _____ of
    impression material beyond the occlusal surfaces and incisal
    edges of the teeth.

    (a) 1 to 2 mm
    (b) 2 to 3 mm
    (c) 3 to 4 mm
    (d) 4 to 5 mm

PROCEDURE: OBTAINING A MANDIBULAR ALGINATE IMPRESSION		
GOAL: The student will obtain an acceptable alginate impression of the mandibular arch to include the anatomic and dental landmarks. (An acceptable impression meets the criteria outlined in the text or as specified by the instructor.)		
SE = Student evaluation C = Criterion met IE = Instructor evaluation X = Criterion not met	SE	IE
1. Instruments and Materials: alginate powder, room temperature water, measuring devices for the water and powder, flexible rubber mixing bowl, spatula, perforated mandibular tray (sized to fit the patient's mouth), peripheral wax and paper towels.		
2. Seated and draped patient. Informed patient of procedure and, if present, removed removable prosthesis.		
3. Washed hands. Selected tray and modified borders with wax.		
4. Asked patient to rinse mouth (to remove debris).		
5. Mixed alginate to homogeneous mix in less than one minute.		
6. Loaded tray, smoothed surface of alginate with finger moistened with water.		
7. Spread alginate on occlusal and interproximal surfaces of mandibular teeth and positioned tray.		
8. Allowed material to set and removed tray without damage to the impression or discomfort to the patient.		
9. Stored the impression until it could be poured. Finished taking impressions, cleaned up all equipment and materials and returned them to storage.		
Comments:		

PROCEDURE: OBTAINING A MAXILLARY ALGINATE IMPRESSION		
GOAL: The student will obtain an acceptable alginate impression of the maxillary arch to include the anatomic and dental landmarks. (An acceptable impression meets the criteria outlined in the text or as specified by the instructor.)		
SE = Student evaluation C = Criterion met IE = Instructor evaluation X = Criterion not met	SE	IE
1. **Instruments and Materials:** alginate powder, room temperature water, measuring devices for the water and powder, flexible rubber mixing bowl, spatula, perforated maxillary tray (sized to fit the patient's mouth), peripheral wax and paper towels.		
2. Seated and draped patient. Informed patient of procedure and, if present, removed removable prosthesis.		
3. Washed hands. Selected maxillary tray and modified borders with wax.		
4. Asked patient to rinse mouth (to remove debris).		
5. Mixed alginate to homogeneous mix in no more than one minute.		
6. Loaded tray, smoothed surface of alginate with finger moistened with water.		
7. Spread alginate on occlusal and interproximal surfaces of maxillary teeth and positioned tray.		
8. Allowed material to set and removed tray without damage to the impression or discomfort to the patient.		
9. Optional: If both maxillary and mandibular impressions were taken, completed tongue space of mandibular impression while maxillary impression was setting in patient's mouth.		
10. Stored the impression until it could be poured. Finished taking impressions, cleaned up all materials and equipment and returned them to storage.		

PROCEDURE: OBTAINING A WAX BITE REGISTRATION		
GOAL: The student will obtain a wax bite registration of the patient's maxillary and mandibular dentition in centric occlusion.		
SE = Student evaluation C = Criterion met IE = Instructor evaluation X = Criterion not met	SE	IE
1. **Instruments and Materials:** preformed wax bite registration wafers, bunsen burner, and matches.		
2. Washed hands and informed patient of the procedure.		
3. Examined the patient's oral cavity. If present, removed removable prosthesis. Asked patient to rinse mouth and remove debris.		
4. Selected wax wafer and warmed slightly over flame of bunsen burner.		
5. Placed wax wafer on occlusal surfaces of mandibular teeth.		
6. Directed patient to close normally (in centric occlusion).		
7. Adapted wax margin to facial surfaces of teeth.		
8. Allowed wax to cool. Asked patient to open mouth. Removed wax wafer without distortion and placed wax bite registration aside.		
9. Checked patient's dentition for excess wax and asked patient to rinse mouth.		
Comments:		

PROCEDURE: PRODUCING STUDY CASTS IN DENTAL PLASTER		
GOAL: Using the pouring procedure specified by the instructor, the student will produce acceptable study casts in dental plaster. (An acceptable study cast will meet the criteria specified in the text or as established by the instructor.)		
SE = Student evaluation C = Criterion met IE = Instructor evaluation X = Criterion not met	SE	IE
1. **Instruments and Materials:** alginate impression(s), dental plaster, room temperature water, scales and devices for measuring water and powder, flexible mixing bowl and spatula, a vibrator with a paper cover. Note, additional materials may be needed depending upon the pouring procedure to be followed.		
2. Checked impression for acceptability. If necessary, rinsed to removed any debris, blood or saliva.		
3. Measured materials to be used.		
4. Mixed and vibrated dental plaster to homogeneous consistency within two minutes.		
5. Used small, continuous increments to pour and complete the impression according to the selected pouring procedure.		
6. Cleaned bowl and spatula. Returned supplies to storage space. Left work area neat and ready for use.		
Comments:		

LEARNING GOALS

The student will be able to:

1. Describe the limitations and uses of coronal polishing technique (as opposed to a prophylaxis).

2. Identify and describe the functions of the instruments and materials used in coronal polishing.

3. Describe the care of dental appliances (prostheses).

4. Demonstrate coronal polishing on a manikin or patient.

5. Demonstrate the care and lubrication of the right-angle handpiece.

EXERCISES

1. The _____ stain found on some children's teeth may be the retention of Nasmyth's membrane and food debris.

   (a) black
   (b) green
   (c) orange
   (d) red

2. _____ is used for removal of light stains on the tooth enamel.

   (a) Pumice
   (b) Silex
   (c) Super-fine silex
   (d) Zirconium silicate

3. A _____ is the powered control of the handpiece.

   (a) fulcrum
   (b) porte polisher
   (c) rheostat
   (d) thermostat

4. The rubber cup is used as a dry polishing accessory.

   (a) true
   (b) false

5. To clean the facial surfaces of the maxillary right quadrant,
   the patient's head to turned toward the _____.

   (a) left
   (b) right

6. When polishing the lingual surfaces of the maxillary anteriors,
   the operator is at the _____ position.

   (a) 8-o'clock
   (b) 9-o'clock
   (c) 10-o'clock
   (d) 11-o'clock

7. _____ stains are found within the enamel and cannot be removed
   by polishing.

   (a) Extrinsic
   (b) Intrinsic

8. To avoid injury to the gingival margin the rubber polishing cup
   is directed _____ the gingiva.

   (a) away from
   (b) toward

9. A bristle brush should be used on a gold restoration to enhance
   the shine.

   (a) true
   (b) false

10. When polishing the lingual surfaces of the mandibular right
    quadrant, the patient's head is turned to the _____.

    (a) left
    (b) right

11. During coronal polishing, when the operator is seated at the
    9-o'clock position, the assistant is seated at the _____
    position.

    (a) 2-o'clock
    (b) 3-o'clock
    (c) 4-o'clock
    (d) B or C

12. Always use _____ revolutions of the polishing cup or the bristle brush.

    (a) high-speed
    (b) low-speed

13. Working at the 11-o'clock position, the operator uses _____ vision when polishing the lingual surfaces of the mandibular teeth.

    (a) direct
    (b) indirect

14. A complete denture is cleaned in the mouth.

    (a) true
    (b) false

15. The right-angle handpiece is _____.

    (a) disassembled for cleaning.
    (b) lubricated with petroleum jelly.
    (c) sterilized by autoclaving.
    (d) A, B and C

16. If scaling the teeth is indicated prior to polishing, the _____ performs the scaling.

    (a) DDS
    (b) EFDA or RDA
    (c) RDH
    (d) A or C

17. Teeth are polished prior to _____.

    (a) application of topical fluoride.
    (b) cementation of crowns or bridges.
    (c) placement of rubber dam.
    (d) A, B and C

18. The operator requests the patient to keep his eyes _____ throughout the procedure.

    (a) closed
    (b) open

19. A _____ is used to remove plaque and stain from the interproximal areas.

   (a) bristle brush
   (b) floss threader
   (c) porte polisher
   (d) rubber cup

20. The areas of a denture which do not contact the oral tissues may be polished using a very moist polishing agent with a right-angle handpiece and rubber cup.

   (a) true
   (b) false

21. A _____ is used to polish the occlusal surfaces.

   (a) bristle brush
   (b) porte polisher
   (c) rubber cup
   (d) B or C

22. The polishing cup is used with a _____ motion.

   (a) lifting
   (b) stroking
   (c) wiping
   (d) A, B and C

23. The right-angle handpiece is held with a _____ grasp.

   (a) modified pen
   (b) palm-thumb
   (c) pen
   (d) reverse palm-thumb

24. The lingual surfaces of the maxillary right quadrant are polished with the patient's head in the _____ position.

   (a) left
   (b) right

25. The flossing procedure begins at the distal of tooth # _____.

   (a) 1
   (b) 16
   (c) 17
   (d) 32

PROCEDURE: CORONAL POLISHING PROCEDURE (with operator at 9-o'clock position, patient in head-left position)		
GOAL: The student will perform, on a manikin or on a patient, coronal polishing procedure including all surfaces of the erupted dentition in the following areas: (1) facial surfaces of the maxillary right quadrant, (2) lingual surfaces of the maxillary left quadrant, (3) facial surfaces of the mandibular right quadrant and (4) the lingual surfaces of the mandibular left quadrant.		
SE = Student evaluation C = Criterion met IE = Instructor evaluation X = Criterion not met	SE	IE
1. **Instruments and Materials:** mouth mirror and explorer, disclosing agent, right angle handpiece (RAH), rubber cup, bristle brush, polishing agent, dental floss and tape.		
2. Seated and draped patient. Washed hands and explained procedure to patient. Used disclosing agent to disclose plaque.		
3. Placed self at 9-o'clock position and patient in head-left position.		
4. Placed rubber cup on RAH. Picked up polishing paste on rubber cup. Placed paste on tooth surfaces.		
5. Held the RAH with a modified pen grasp and established a fulcrum on quadrant of the teeth being polished.		
6. Rotated the rubber cup at slow speed. Placed rotating cup on facial surface of posterior teeth. Moved rotating cup with light, lifting and wiping strokes.		
7. Replenished polishing paste on rubber cup throughout the procedure.		
8. Maintained patient comfort, tissue integrity and a dry working field.		
Comments:		

PROCEDURE: CORONAL POLISHING PROCEDURE (with operator at 9-o'clock position, patient in head-right position)		
GOAL: The student will perform, on a manikin or on a patient, coronal polishing procedure including all surfaces of the erupted dentition in the following areas: (1) facial surfaces of the maxillary left quadrant, (2) lingual surfaces of the maxillary right quadrant, (3) facial surfaces of the mandibular left quadrant and (4) the lingual surfaces of the mandibular right quadrant. **Note:** If the student is polishing the entire dentition, steps 1 and 2 will not be repeated.		
SE = Student evaluation C = Criterion met IE = Instructor evaluation X = Criterion not met	SE	IE
1. **Instruments and Materials:** mouth mirror and explorer, disclosing agent, right angle handpiece (RAH), rubber cup, bristle brush, polishing agent, dental floss and tape.		
2. Seated and draped patient. Washed hands and explained procedure to patient. Used disclosing agent to disclose plaque.		
3. Placed self at 9-o'clock position and patient in head-right position.		
4. Placed rubber cup on RAH. Picked up polishing paste on rubber cup. Placed paste on tooth surfaces.		
5. Held the RAH with a modified pen grasp and established a fulcrum on quadrant of the teeth being polished.		
6. Rotated the rubber cup at slow speed. Placed rotating cup on facial surface of posterior teeth. Moved rotating cup with light, lifting and wiping strokes.		
7. Replenished polishing paste on rubber cup throughout the procedure.		
8. Maintained patient comfort, tissue integrity and a dry working field.		

PROCEDURE: CORONAL POLISHING PROCEDURE (with operator at 11-o'clock or 12-o'clock position)		
GOAL: The student will perform, on a manikin or on a patient, coronal polishing procedure including all surfaces of the erupted dentition in the following areas: (1) lingual surfaces of the mandibular anteriors, (2) lingual surfaces of the maxillary anteriors and (3) facial surfaces of the maxillary anteriors. **Note:** If the student is polishing the entire dentition, steps 1 and 2 will not be repeated.		
SE = Student evaluation C = Criterion met IE = Instructor evaluation X = Criterion not met	SE	IE
1. **Instruments and Materials:** mouth mirror and explorer, disclosing agent, right angle handpiece (RAH), rubber cup, bristle brush, polishing agent, dental floss and tape.		
2. Seated and draped patient. Washed hands and explained procedure to patient. Used disclosing agent to disclose plaque.		
3. Placed self at 11-o'clock or 12-o'clock position and requested patient to straighten his head and to tilt his chin upward.		
4. Placed rubber cup on RAH. Picked up polishing paste on rubber cup. Placed paste on tooth surfaces.		
5. Held the RAH with a modified pen grasp and established a fulcrum on quadrant of the teeth being polished.		
6. Rotated the rubber cup at slow speed. Placed rotating cup on facial surface of posterior teeth. Moved rotating cup with light, lifting and wiping strokes.		
7. Replenished polishing paste on rubber cup throughout the procedure.		
8. Maintained patient comfort, tissue integrity and a dry working field.		

PROCEDURE: CORONAL POLISHING PROCEDURE (facial surfaces of the mandibular anteriors, and occlusal surfaces with operator at 9-o'clock position)		
GOAL: The student will perform, on a manikin or on a patient, coronal polishing procedure including the facial surfaces of the mandibular anteriors and the occlusal surfaces of all surfaces of the erupted dentition. **Note:** If the student is polishing the entire dentition, steps 1 and 2 will not be repeated.		
SE = Student evaluation C = Criterion met IE = Instructor evaluation X = Criterion not met	SE	IE
1. **Instruments and Materials:** mouth mirror and explorer, disclosing agent, right angle handpiece (RAH), rubber cup, bristle brush, polishing agent, dental floss and tape.		
2. Seated and draped patient. Washed hands and explained procedure to patient. Used disclosing agent to disclose plaque.		
3. Placed self at 9-o'clock position and polished facial surface of the mandibular anteriors.		
4. Placed bristle brush on RAH. Held the RAH with a modified pen grasp and established a fulcrum for the teeth being polished.		
5. Picked up polishing paste on bristle brush. Kept polishing paste on bristle brush throughout procedure.		
6. Rotated and moved the bristle brush at slow speed over the grooves of the occlusal surfaces in the following sequence: the maxillary right quadrant, mandibular right quadrant, maxillary left quadrant and mandibular left quadrant. (Did not use bristle brush on gold restorations.)		
7. Maintained patient comfort, tissue integrity and a dry working field.		

PROCEDURE: CORONAL POLISHING PROCEDURE (interproximal surfaces)		
GOAL: The student will perform, on a manikin or on a patient, coronal polishing procedure on the interproximal surfaces of the erupted dentition. Note: If the student is polishing the entire dentition, steps 1 and 2 will not be repeated.		
SE = Student evaluation C = Criterion met IE = Instructor evaluation X = Criterion not met	SE	IE
1. Instruments and Materials: mouth mirror and explorer, disclosing agent, dental floss and tape, porte polisher and polishing agent.		
2. Seated and draped patient. Washed hands and explained procedure to patient. Used disclosing agent to disclose plaque.		
3. Used floss to clean interproximal areas beginning with the distal surface of tooth #32 and proceeding to the distal of tooth #1.		
5. If plaque and stain remained, used a porte-polisher with polishing agent to polish interproximal surfaces.		
6. Maintained patient comfort, tissue integrity and a dry working field.		
7. Rinsed and vacuumed oral cavity to assure patient comfort.		
8. Applied disclosing solution again. Teeth cleared of plaque and debris.		
Comments:		

LEARNING GOALS

The student will be able to:

1. State the indications for use of rubber dam.

2. Describe the specialized types of rubber dam and rubber dam clamps.

3. Describe the technique used for rubber dam placement around a fixed bridge.

4. Demonstrate punching rubber dam for placement on single or multiple upper or lower anterior or posterior teeth.

5. Demonstrate proper placement, inversion and removal of rubber dam on a manikin or patient.

EXERCISES

1. _____ rubber dam clamps are designed without extra projections to aid in holding the dam.

   (a) Modified
   (b) Posterior
   (c) Winged
   (d) Wingless

2. When placing the rubber dam clamp, the _____ jaw of the clamp serves as a fulcrum for placement of the facial jaw.

   (a) cervical
   (b) distal
   (c) lingual
   (d) mesial

3. _____ may be used to stabilize the rubber dam on the last tooth exposed at the end of the arch opposite the tooth to be operated upon.

   (a) A cotton roll
   (b) A small piece of rubber dam
   (c) Compound
   (d) The rubber dam napkin

4. To provide patient comfort following placement of a rubber dam, the assistant may _____ .

   (a) dry the teeth with warm air.
   (b) rinse the teeth with warm water.
   (c) place a saliva ejector under the dam.
   (d) raise the patient's head.

5. The number _____ hole on the rubber dam punch plate is used for placement of a rubber dam over a long-span fixed bridge.

   (a) 2
   (b) 3
   (c) 4
   (d) 5

6. For a Class V restoration, the punch hole should be placed _____ from the normal location.

   (a) distally
   (b) facially
   (c) lingually
   (d) mesially

7. Placing the _____ rubber dam frame involves passing the strap around the back of the patient's head.

   (a) Ferrier
   (b) Hollenback
   (c) Woodbury
   (d) Young's

8. The _____ rubber dam frame may be placed with, or without, a rubber dam napkin.

   (a) Ferrier
   (b) Hollenback
   (c) Woodbury
   (d) Young's

9. When removing the rubber dam, suture scissors are used to cut the dam _____ the rubber dam clamp has been removed.

   (a) after
   (b) before

10. _____ is used to stabilize a Ferrier separator for a Class V preparation.

    (a) Cold cure acrylic
    (b) Periphery wax
    (c) Red compound
    (d) Sticky wax

11. In the process of removing the rubber dam, scissors are used to sever _____.

    (a) each septum of the dam.
    (b) the attachment to the dam frame.
    (c) the rubber dam napkin.
    (d) A and B

12. Following the removal of the rubber dam clamp, the _____ is massaged to increase circulation.

    (a) cementoenamel junction
    (b) gingiva
    (c) interproximal contact
    (d) periosteum

13. Following removal, the rubber dam is reassembled to _____.

    (a) check the extent of the restoration.
    (b) detect that the entire rubber dam has been removed.
    (c) determine the condition of the gingiva.
    (d) prepare for the sterilization procedure.

14. _____ rubber dam is preferred by some operators because it withstands abuse when placed over crowns, fixed bridges or teeth with close contacts.

    (a) Dark heavy-weight
    (b) Dark light-weight
    (c) Gray light-weight
    (d) Green heavy-weight

15. _____ clamps retract the gingiva and permit visibility of facial cavities.

    (a) Anterior
    (b) Cervical
    (c) Pedodontic
    (d) Posterior

16. Just prior to placement, the holes on the tooth surface side of the rubber dam are lubricated lightly with _____.

    (a) petroleum jelly
    (b) shaving cream
    (c) zinc oxide ointment
    (d) A or B

17. A _____ rubber dam is used for children's teeth.

    (a) 4" x 5"
    (b) 5" x 5"
    (c) 5" x 6"
    (d) 6" x 6"

18. A ragged hole in the rubber dam will _____.

    (a) irritate the gingiva
    (b) slip off the clamp
    (c) tear easily
    (d) A and C

19. When punching the rubber dam, generally allow _____ mm. of rubber dam between the holes of the dam.

    (a) 2.0 to 2.5
    (b) 2.5 to 3.0
    (c) 3.0 to 3.5
    (d) 3.5 to 4.0

20. The _____ hole in the rubber dam is placed over the tooth holding the rubber dam clamp.

    (a) anchor
    (b) cervical
    (c) clamp
    (d) key punch

21. A _____ suture needle is used in placing rubber dam over a fixed bridge.

    (a) dulled
    (b) sharpened

22. _____ may be used (optionally) to lubricate the patient's lips prior to rubber dam placement.

    (a) Petroleum jelly
    (b) Shaving cream
    (c) Zinc oxide ointment
    (d) A or C

23. When preparing to punch the rubber dam, if anterior teeth are to be clamped, the dam is held with the _____ border toward the operator.

    (a) inferior
    (b) superior

24. The first time the rubber dam forceps and clamps are passed to the operator without the rubber dam itself.

    (a) true
    (b) false

25. The operator uses a _____ to invert the edges of the rubber dam around the lingual and facial surfaces of the teeth to be exposed.

    (a) beavertail burnisher
    (b) finishing knife
    (c) separator wrench
    (d) spoon excavator

PROCEDURE: PUNCHING RUBBER DAM		
GOAL: The student will punch rubber dam for placement over teeth as specified by the operator (or instructor).		
SE = Student evaluation C = Criterion met IE = Instructor evaluation X = Criterion not met	SE	IE
1. **Instruments and Materials:** rubber dam, rubber dam punch, rubber dam template or rubber dam stamp (optional).		
2. Positioned stylus of the punch to assure that the holes punched were clean, round and that the punch stylus was not dulled.		
3. Positioned holes away from the edges of the dam according to the teeth to be included in the dam application.		
4. Holes were the correct size for the teeth being exposed.		
5. Distance between holes, and curvature of the arch, permitted smooth application of the dam without folds or excessive stretching.		
6. Allowed for malaligned teeth.		
Comments:		

PROCEDURE: PLACEMENT OF RUBBER DAM		
GOAL: The student will place a rubber dam on a manikin or patient. The teeth to be exposed will be determined by the instructor.		
SE = Student evaluation C = Criterion met IE = Instructor evaluation X = Criterion not met	SE	IE
1. Instruments and Materials: mirror, explorer, cotton pliers, previously punched rubber dam, rubber dam clamps with 18" ligature tied to the bow of each clamp, rubber dam clamp forceps, rubber dam holder and napkin (if indicated), lubricant, ligature, beavertail burnisher, stabilization materials and air syringe.		
2. Stabilized clamp fit on cementoenamel junction of tooth. Avoided gingival impingement.		
3. Lubricated rubber dam on tissue side.		
4. Placed dam and clamp.		
5. Placed and adjusted the frame.		
6. Passed ligature (floss) between proximal contacts of adjacent teeth. Rubber dam septum moved toward the gingiva.		
7. Ligated rubber dam at last punch hole (opposite side of tooth to be operated upon).		
8. Inverted rubber dam around cervix of each tooth.		
Comments:		

PROCEDURE: REMOVAL OF RUBBER DAM		
GOAL: The student will remove the rubber dam while maintaining patient comfort.		
SE = Student evaluation C = Criterion met IE = Instructor evaluation X = Criterion not met	SE	IE
1. Instruments and Materials: mirror, explorer, cotton pliers, rubber dam clamp forceps, suture scissors, finishing knife, dental floss, warm water syringe, mouth rinse, vacuum tip, and cleansing tissues.		
2. Severed ligature with finishing knife.		
3. Used suture scissors to cut each rubber dam septum. Worked from posterior to anterior.		
4. Removed rubber dam clamp.		
5. Removed rubber dam holder.		
6. Removed rubber dam (and napkin if used). Checked for tears or missing pieces.		
7. Wiped patient's face clean.		
8. Massaged gingiva to increase circulation.		
9. Assisted patient in rinsing mouth, vacuumed debris and fluids from oral cavity.		
Comments:		

LEARNING GOALS

The student will be able to:

1. Describe the principles of cavity preparation using the appropriate terminology.

2. Describe the use of composite and direct-filling resins for tooth restorations.

3. Identify the components of a Tofflemire matrix retainer and band. Demonstrate preparation, placement and removal of the retainer and band.

4. Demonstrate the process of dispensing and triturating amalgam for restorations.

5. Describe placing, condensing, carving and polishing amalgam restorations.

6. Describe the technique for obtaining a direct inlay pattern.

7. Describe the types and uses of direct gold restorations and differentiate between cohesive and noncohesive gold.

8. Demonstrate the preparation and application of dental cements, cavity liners, varnishes and bases in operative dentistry.

EXERCISES:

1. In operative dentistry, zinc phosphate cement is used _____.

   (a) as a surgical dressing.
   (b) for the cementation of permanent restorations.
   (c) for the cementation of temporary coverage.
   (d) in place of a cavity liner.

2. In a cavity preparation, a/an _____ angle is formed by the junction of two walls (tooth surfaces).

   (a) axial
   (b) incisal
   (c) line
   (d) point

3. Zinc oxide-eugenol cement is used as a _____.

   (a) base under composite restorations
   (b) cement for temporary crowns
   (c) sedative base
   (d) B and C

4. _____ is used to remove zinc phosphate cement mix that has hardened on a glass slab.

   (a) Bicarbonate of soda
   (b) Citric acid
   (c) Eugenol
   (d) Hydrogen peroxide

5. Polycarboxylate (polyacrylate) cement forms a bond with the _____.

   (a) cementum
   (b) dentin
   (c) pulp
   (d) root

6. Cavity varnish is applied to seal the _____ in the cavity preparation.

   (a) cementoblasts
   (b) dentinal tubules
   (c) enamel fibers
   (d) pulp horns

7. Direct-filling restorative resins may be placed using the _____ method.

   (a) brush
   (b) flow
   (c) pressure
   (d) A, B or C

8. _____ is used in the etching of enamel margins in preparation for a composite restoration.

   (a) 40% phosphoric acid solution
   (b) 80% ammonia
   (c) 90% isopropyl alcohol
   (d) 100% hydrogen peroxide

Answer the following questions based on the diagram at the right.

9. This is the _____.

   (a) inner nut (knob)
   (b) outer guide slot
   (c) outer nut (knob)
   (d) spindle

10. This is the _____.

   (a) guide slot
   (b) inner nut (knob)
   (c) outer nut (knob)
   (d) vise

11. This is the _____.

   (a) inner nut (knob)
   (b) outer guide slot
   (c) spindle
   (d) vise

12. This is the _____.

   (a) inner guide slot
   (b) outer guide slot
   (c) outer nut (knob)
   (d) pin

13. This is placed _____ the gingiva.

   (a) away from
   (b) toward

14. The _____ is used to adjust the size of the band.

   (a) guide slot
   (b) inner nut (knob)
   (c) outer nut (knob)
   (d) spindle

15. The _____ flange of the band is placed toward the gingiva.

   (a) larger
   (b) smaller

16. _____ is/are used to provide added retention in an extensive amalgam restoration.

(a) A cement base
(b) A matrix
(c) Pins
(d) A sealant adhesive

17. A/an _____ is used to place the triturated silver amalgam in the cavity preparation.

(a) amalgam carrier
(b) discoid/cleoid carrier
(c) Hollenback carver
(d) spoon excavator

18. The operator uses a/an _____ to carve the primary grooves on the occlusal surface of a freshly placed amalgam restoration.

(a) discoid/cleoid
(b) explorer
(c) Hollenback carver
(d) interproximal carver

19. After 48 hours, _____ is used for the final polishing of the recently placed amalgam restoration.

(a) laboratory pumice
(b) silex paste
(c) tin oxide
(d) B and C

20. A/an _____ is a cast restoration designed to restore the interproximal and two or more cusps of a posterior tooth.

(a) abutment
(b) crown
(c) onlay
(d) pontic

21. _____ cement is mixed within a small area on the slab, using the spatula in a rocking action. The total manipulation time is 30 seconds and the completed mix resembles wet sand.

(a) EBA
(b) Silicate
(c) Zinc oxide-eugenol
(d) Zinc phosphate

22. A custom matrix band for an amalgam restoration in a posterior tooth may be prepared from _____.

    (a) acrylic
    (b) cellophane
    (c) self polymerizing acrylic
    (d) stainless steel

23. Annealing noncohesive gold foil is the process used to remove _____.

    (a) ammonia gases
    (b) contamination
    (c) surface oxides
    (d) tarnish

24. Ortho-ethoxybenzoic acid (EBA) cement is used for _____.

    (a) a base under a composite restoration.
    (b) a temporary restoration.
    (c) neutralizing the effect of phosphoric acid.
    (d) permanent cementation of inlays and crowns.

25. _____ is placed with a cotton pellet.

    (a) Calcium hydroxide
    (b) Copal varnish
    (c) Glass ionomer
    (d) Resin cement

26. The mercury/alloy ratio is _____ spill(s) of mercury to one pellet of alloy.

    (a) 1
    (b) 2
    (c) 3
    (d) 4

27. In the _____ technique the wax pattern is waxed in the oral cavity.

    (a) direct
    (b) indirect

28. Gold foil should be annealed at least twice before use.

    (a) true
    (b) false

29. The consistency of zinc phosphate cement is correct for _____ when the mix will fall from the spatula in an elongated droplet.

    (a) an insulating base
    (b) cementation

30. After the amalgam restoration has been placed, the _____ is removed first.

    (a) matrix band
    (b) matrix band holder
    (c) wedge

31. Amalgam is mulled by rolling it in the fingers.

    (a) true
    (b) false

32. _____ cement should not be used if the mix has reached the stringy or tacky stage on the slab.

    (a) Glass ionomer
    (b) Ortho-ethoxybenzoic
    (c) Polycarboxylate
    (d) Silicophosphate

33. Patients with a _____ should be cautioned against biting hard substances, such as ice, that could fracture it.

    (a) class V amalgam restoration
    (b) composite veneer
    (c) gold foil inlay
    (d) silicate restoration

34. The procedure of condensing and overlapping gold foil is referred to as stepping.

    (a) true
    (b) false

35. A _____ is the slanting of the enamel margins of a tooth cavity.

    (a) bevel
    (b) cavosurface angle
    (c) dovetail
    (d) A and C

PROCEDURE: PREPARE A MIX OF ZINC PHOSPHATE CEMENT (FOR CEMENTATION)		
GOALS: The student will prepare a mix of zinc phosphate cement for cementation.		
SE = Student evaluation C = Criterion met IE = Instructor evaluation X = Criterion not met	SE	IE
1. **Instruments and Materials:** glass slab (68°F), flexible spatula, cement powder and liquid with dispensers.		
2. Dispensed 2 measures of powder on the right two-thirds of the glass slab and divided it into small increments.		
3. Dispensed 2 drops of liquid on left one-third of the glass slab. Expelled excess liquid into bottle and tightly replaced cap.		
4. Used a figure-eight rotary motion to slowly incorporate a small amount of powder into liquid.		
5. Completed additional powder increments and mixing within 90 seconds.		
6. Tested mass for droplet break one inch from slab.		
7. Cleaned slab and spatula and put materials away.		
Comments:		

PROCEDURE: PREPARE A MIX OF ZINC PHOSPHATE CEMENT (FOR INSULATING BASE)		
GOALS: The student will prepare a mix of zinc phosphate cement for an insulating base.		
SE = Student evaluation C = Criterion met IE = Instructor evaluation X = Criterion not met	SE	IE
1. **Instruments and Materials:** glass slab (68°F), flexible spatula, cement powder and liquid with dispensers.		
2. Dispensed 2 measures of powder on the right two-thirds of the glass slab and divided into small segments.		
3. Dispensed 2 drops of liquid on left one-third of the glass slab. Expelled excess liquid into bottle and tightly replaced cap.		
4. Used a figure-eight rotary motion to slowly incorporate a small initial amount of powder into liquid.		
5. Completed additional powder increments and mixing within 90 seconds.		
6. Completed mass of putty-like consistency.		
7. Cleaned slab and spatula and put materials away.		
Comments:		

PROCEDURE: PREPARE A MIX OF ZINC OXIDE-EUGENOL CEMENT (FOR SEDATIVE BASE)		
GOALS: The student will prepare a mix of zinc oxide-eugenol cement for a sedative base.		
SE = Student evaluation C = Criterion met IE = Instructor evaluation X = Criterion not met	SE	IE
1. Instruments and Materials: paper pad, flexible spatula, cement powder and liquid with dispensers.		
2. Dispensed 1 scoop of powder onto the paper pad.		
3. Dispensed 1 drop of liquid onto the paper pad. Expelled excess liquid into bottle and tightly replaced cap.		
4. Used the spatula flat on its side to incorporate a medium amount (1/2 scoop) of powder into liquid.		
5. Spatulated this together in a small area.		
6. Incorporated more powder and spatulated in a small area.		
7. Completed homogeneous mix, of a putty-like consistency, within 45 seconds.		
8. Removed used materials, cleaned spatula and put materials away.		
Comments:		

PROCEDURE: PREPARE, PLACE AND WEDGE A TOFFLEMIRE RETAINER		
GOALS: The student will prepare, place and wedge a Tofflemire matrix on a posterior tooth (on a typodont).		
SE = Student evaluation C = Criterion met IE = Instructor evaluation X = Criterion not met	SE	IE
1. **Instruments and Materials:** Tofflemire matrix retainer and assorted molar bands, ball burnisher, paper pad, wooden wedge, hemostat.		
2. Selected and fitted matrix band. Placed band in retainer (occlusal edge first).		
3. Placed matrix band and retainer over the crown of the prepared tooth. Tightened to hold securely in place while maintaining patient comfort.		
4. Selected, modified and placed wedge in beaks of hemostat.		
5. Placed wedge in interproximal space below gingival margin of tooth preparation from the lingual side. Wedge slightly opened contact with adjacent teeth.		
6. After restoration completed: removed wedge with hemostat, removed matrix holder and removed band without fracturing restoration and while maintaining patient comfort.		
Comments:		

LEARNING GOALS

The student will be able to:

1. Describe a complete dental examination and oral disease control program for a child patient.

2. Describe the use of premedication and pain control in pedodontics.

3. Describe the following: use of preventive resin restorations; the classification and treatment of fractured teeth; placement of a stainless steel crown and the specialized oral surgery needs of children.

4. Describe the construction and use of custom mouth guards, bite planes and space maintainers.

5. Demonstrate the application of topical fluoride using a commercial fluoride gel and trays.

6. Demonstrate the application of pit and fissure sealants.

7. Demonstrate fabrication, placement and stabilization of a "T" matrix.

EXERCISES

1. Film size(s) _____ is/are used for a radiographic series on a preschool child.

    (a) 0.5
    (b) 0
    (c) 1
    (d) B and C

2. The trays prepared with topical fluoride solution are placed on clean teeth and left in place for _____ minutes.

    (a) 1 to 2
    (b) 3 to 4
    (c) 4 to 5
    (d) 5 to 6

3. _____ is one of the indications for use of pit and fissure
   sealants for pedodontic patients.

   (a) Decalcification
   (b) Deep pits and narrow fissures
   (c) Incipient caries
   (d) Instrinsic stains

4. To aid the child in distress from pain or fear during dental
   treatment, the pedodontist may premedicate the patient
   immediately prior to treatment.

   (a) true
   (b) false

5. A/an _____ may be used as a custom matrix for a child patient.

   (a) cellophane strip
   (b) Ivory holder
   (c) T-band
   (d) Tofflemire

6. Preformed stainless steel crowns are indicated for teeth that
   are _____.

   (a) badly decayed
   (b) fractured
   (c) malformed
   (d) A, B and C

7. After coronal polishing, and before application of the pit and
   fissure sealant, the teeth are _____.

   (a) acid etched.
   (b) coated with a sealant.
   (c) filled with resin.
   (d) treated with topical fluoride.

8. A class _____ fracture involves the enamel, dentin and pulp of
   the tooth.

   (a) 1
   (b) 2
   (c) 3
   (d) 4

9. _____ is used for a tooth with deep caries when there is danger
   of pulpal exposure.

   (a) Direct pulp capping
   (b) Indirect pulp capping
   (c) Pulpectomy
   (d) Pulpotomy

10. A/an _____ is the mechanical, radical removal of the vital
    portion of the tooth pulp.

    (a) apicoectomy
    (b) pulp capping
    (c) vital pulpectomy
    (d) vital pulpotomy

11. A _____ is a device fabricated of acrylic to retain fractured,
    loosened and evulsed teeth.

    (a) bite block
    (b) bite plane
    (c) retainer
    (d) splint

12. _____ are fabricated for participants in contact sports.

    (a) Bite planes
    (b) Mouth guards
    (c) Splints
    (d) Retainers

13. Following premature loss of a primary tooth, _____ are designed
    to maintain the space until the normal eruption of the
    subsequent permanent tooth.

    (a) bite blocks
    (b) bite planes
    (c) mouth guards
    (d) space maintainers

14. Prenatal and natal history provides a background for
    understanding the physical and dental growth and development of
    the child.

    (a) true
    (b) false

15. The first step in the construction of a splint for traumatized teeth is to _____ .

    (a) adjust the occlusion
    (b) extract the teeth
    (c) obtain an alginate impression
    (d) perform a pulpotomy

16. A heavy _____ attachment may cause a diastema between the maxillary anterior teeth.

    (a) frenal
    (b) gingival
    (c) lingual
    (d) mucosal

17. A/an _____ may be used instead of pit and fissure sealant for teeth that are decalcified in the pits and fissures.

    (a) amalgam restoration
    (b) fluoride treatment
    (c) preventive resin restoration
    (d) silicate restoration

18. _____ is a process that modifies and tightens the fit of a stainless steel crown by pinching in the margin.

    (a) Contouring
    (b) Crimping
    (c) Scribing
    (d) Spot welding

19. The pedodontic patient is referred back to the general dentist _____ .

    (a) after all caries have been treated.
    (b) after the exfoliation of the anterior primary teeth.
    (c) following the eruption of the permanent dentition.
    (d) when the child reaches grade school age.

20. During the application of topical fluorides the child should be encouraged to _____ .

    (a) hold his breath.
    (b) not swallow any of the solution.
    (c) rinse his mouth thoroughly.
    (d) swish the excess solution around his mouth.

21. Rubber dam _____ indicated for use in the treatment of children's teeth.

    (a) is
    (b) is not

22. When an emergency occurs involving a fractured or evulsed tooth, the patient should be directed to come to the office _____.

    (a) as soon as is convenient.
    (b) immediately.
    (c) right after school.
    (d) within the next 24 hours.

23. In a vital pulpotomy, _____ is/are applied over the calcium hydroxide.

    (a) cavity varnish
    (b) zinc phosphate cement
    (c) zinc oxide-eugenol cement
    (d) B and C

24. A/an _____ space maintainer is designed to retain the space for several unerupted teeth missing in both quadrants of the same dental arch.

    (a) band and loop
    (b) fixed
    (c) occlusal bar
    (d) removable

25. The locking of a permanent tooth out of natural alignment in the arch and toward the tongue or palate is known as _____.

    (a) impaction
    (b) labial version
    (c) lingual version
    (d) overjet

PROCEDURE: APPLICATION OF TOPICAL FLUORIDE		
GOAL: The student will demonstrate application of a topical fluoride gel on a patient or typodont. (The teeth have already received coronal polishing.)		
SE = Student evaluation C = Criterion met IE = Instructor evaluation X = Criterion not met	SE	IE
1. **Instruments and Materials:** commercially prepared fluoride gel, disposable trays and liners, saliva ejector, HVE tip.		
2. Seated patient. Explained the procedure and cautioned the patient not to swallow any of the solution.		
3. Washed hands. Selected trays, placed liners and loaded trays with fluoride gel.		
4. Placed mandibular tray and saliva ejector while maintaining patient comfort. Left tray in place 4 to 5 minutes. Removed tray.		
5. Placed maxillary tray and saliva ejector while maintaining patient comfort. Left tray in place 4 to 5 minutes. Removed tray.		
6. Optional method: both trays may be prepared and placed in the mouth at the same time.		
7. Used HVE to remove excess fluids from the patient's mouth.		
8. Advised patient not to eat, drink or rinse his mouth for 30 minutes. Dismissed patient.		
9. Cleaned up area and materials in preparation for the next patient.		
Comments:		

PROCEDURE: APPLICATION OF PIT AND FISSURE SEALANTS		
GOAL: The student will prepare the teeth and apply pit and fissure sealant to a quadrant of teeth on a pedodontic typodont. (The teeth have previously been polished with a fluoride free abrasive.)		
SE = Student evaluation C = Criterion met IE = Instructor evaluation X = Criterion not met	SE	IE
1. **Instruments and Materials:** Etching liquid, dappen dishes, adhesive sealant and catalyst, cotton pellets, air/water syringe, camel-hair brush, articulating paper, SHP, small round white stone and pedodontic typodont.		
2. Thoroughly dried teeth to receive sealant. Placed a few drops of the etching liquid in a dappen dish.		
3. Used a medium-size cotton pellet to gently dab the etchant on the occlusal surfaces to be treated. Dabbed continuously for approximately 5 seconds after the initial application. Total conditioning time was 60 seconds, plus 10 seconds for each additional tooth.		
4. Sprayed teeth with water to stop etching action. Used warm air to dry etched surfaces.		
5. Prepared sealant material following manufacturer's instructions. Painted sealant on prepared tooth surfaces.		
6. Reapplied where necessary. Completed adaptation of material within 15 seconds.		
7. If indicated, exposed sealant to white-light, following manufacturer's instructions.		
8. Checked patient's occlusion with articulating paper. Adjusted sealant as necessary.		
Comments:		

PROCEDURE: ADAPTING AND PLACING A T-BAND MATRIX		
GOAL: The student will demonstrate preparing and placing a custom T-band matrix on a primary molar on a pedodontic typodont.		
SE = Student evaluation C = Criterion met IE = Instructor evaluation X = Criterion not met	SE	IE
1. **Instruments and Materials:** stainless steel preformed T-band, crown scissors, contouring pliers, wedges, knife, carver, and hemostat and pedodontic typodont.		
2. Selected band and bent the wings to form a U-shaped trough.		
3. Slipped the free end of the band loosely through the "U" formation. Closed the wings and pulled the free end of the band to form a circle.		
4. Placed the band on the tooth with the free end toward the facial surface. Seated and adjusted band. Folded free end to stabilize band size.		
5. Removed band and contoured as necessary. Secured free end, cut off excess band material. Seated completed band.		
6. Used hemostat to place wedge interproximally in the lingual embrasure. Tested wedge with fingers to determine that placement was stable.		
Comments:		

LEARNING GOALS

The student will be able to:

1. Describe the categories of, and need for, orthodontic treatment.
   Also, identify Angle's classification of occlusion and
   malocclusion.

2. Describe the facial habits that may adversely affect orthodontic
   treatment and explain the importance of patient cooperation in
   successful treatment.

3. Describe the principles of tooth movement and identify the types
   of appliances used to achieve this movement.

4. Identify the special instruments used in orthodontic treatment.

5. Describe the role of cephalometrics in orthodontics and identify
   the landmarks of the skull that are important in cephalometrics.

6. Describe the selection, cementation and removal of orthodontic
   bands. Also, describe the procedure used in the direct bonding
   of brackets.

7. Demonstrate the procedure for placement and removal of
   orthodontic separators.

8. Demonstrate pouring, separating, trimming and finishing
   orthodontic study casts.

9. Describe, or demonstrate, the construction of a Hawley retainer.

10. Describe, or demonstrate, the use of the ultrasonic scaler in
    the removal of excess cement.

11. Describe, or demonstrate, placement and removal of arch wires
    and ligature ties.

12. Describe, or demonstrate, giving the patient instructions on
    home care and wearing headgear or a positioner.

EXERCISES

1. When cementing orthodontic bands, a longer setting time for the
   cement is provided by _____.

   (a) adding water to the mix.
   (b) incorporating less powder into the liquid.
   (c) spatulating the mix faster.
   (d) using an extremely cold and dry slab.

2. _____ orthodontics consists of steps taken to prevent or correct problems in the dental arches as they are developing.

   (a) Adjustive
   (b) Corrective
   (c) Interceptive
   (d) Preventive

3. In _____ the mesiobuccal cusp of the maxillary permanent first molar occludes in the buccal groove of the mandibular first molar.

   (a) distoclusion
   (b) labioversion
   (c) linguoversion
   (d) neutroclusion

4. In _____, or mesioclusion, the mandibular arch and the body of the mandible are in bilateral, mesial relationship to the maxillary teeth.

   (a) Class   I occlusion
   (b) Class II occlusion
   (c) Class III occlusion
   (d) neutroclusion

5. The compression of the periodontal ligament in the direction of the desired tooth movement causes _____ of the cells in that area.

   (a) absorption
   (b) deposition
   (c) imbibition
   (d) resorption

6. When applying the etching solution, the operator continuously _____ the enamel surface.

   (a) dabs
   (b) dries
   (c) rubs
   (d) smooths

7. A modified Schwarz plate is a/an _____ orthodontic appliance.

   (a) extraoral
   (b) fixed
   (c) headcap
   (d) removable

8. _____ may be used in the process of changing the position of the tooth.

    (a) Elongating
    (b) Extruding
    (c) Rotating
    (d) Tipping

9. Maxillary premolar bands are first seated on the _____ aspect and then driven over the _____ height of contour.

    (a) facial   mesial
    (b) facial   lingual
    (c) lingual   distal
    (d) lingual   facial

10. _____ are frequently used in minor orthodontic treatment for adults.

    (a) Active retainers
    (b) Dumbbell separators
    (c) Lingual bands
    (d) B and C

11. Direct bonded brackets are removed using a/an _____.

    (a) crown cutter
    (b) pin and ligature cutter
    (c) solvent
    (d) ultrasonic scaler

12. The reaction produced by the _____ force is known as reciprocal force.

    (a) anchorage
    (b) extraoral
    (c) resorption
    (d) rotation

13. Using directly bonded brackets, the light force arch wire is placed within _____ after completion of the final bonding.

    (a) 5 minutes
    (b) 30 minutes
    (c) 3 hours
    (d) 24 hours

14. In the placement of steel spring separators, the _____ of the separator is placed at the interproximal of the lingual surface.

    (a) curved portion
    (b) helix
    (c) pigtail
    (d) short arm

15. Orthodontic bands are cemented on the maxillary centrals 4.0 mm. from the incisal edge as measured with a Boone gauge.

    (a) true
    (b) false

16. The ends of the arch wire are placed in the _____ on the banded posterior molar.

    (a) bonded brackets
    (b) "S" hooks
    (c) seating lugs
    (d) tube slots

17. In selecting bands, the height of the bracket slot _____ essential in determining the position of cuspid bands.

    (a) is
    (b) is not

18. The first step in the removal of the brass wire separators is to lift the _____ of the separator out of the embrasure.

    (a) arm
    (b) helix
    (c) loop
    (d) tail

19. _____ in the acrylic of a Hawley retainer is caused by rapid evaporation of monomer.

    (a) Distortion
    (b) Polymerization
    (c) Porosity
    (d) A and B

20. Angle's _____ occlusion is shown here.

    (a) Class   I
    (b) Class   II, division 1
    (c) Class   II, division 2
    (d) Class III

21. The _____ is a line drawn
    from the superior margin of
    the acoustic meatus to the
    orbitale.

    (a) Bjork's line
    (b) facial line
    (c) Frankfort line
    (d) ramus line

22. Up to the age of five, dentofacial defects do not usually occur
    from the results of _____.

    (a) bruxism
    (b) mouth breathing
    (c) tongue sucking
    (d) thumb and finger sucking

23. Prior to initial placement, preformed ligature wires are bent at
    a _____ angle.

    (a) 25°
    (b) 35°
    (c) 45°
    (d) 90°

24. For the removal of excess cement, the ultrasonic scaler tip is
    placed at a _____ angle to the tooth.

    (a) 10°
    (b) 15°
    (c) 20°
    (d) 25°

25. Patients _____ wear extraoral traction headgear during contact
    sports.

    (a) should
    (b) should not

26. The _____ edge of an orthodontic band is rolled or contoured.

    (a) gingival
    (b) incisal
    (c) occlusal
    (d) B and C

27. _____ separators are placed between anterior contacts with a
    "sawing" or flossing motion.

    (a) Brass wire
    (b) Dumbbell
    (c) Steel spring
    (d) B or C

28. To avoid strong pressure on the tooth, approximately _____ inch
    of the tip of the ultrasonic scaler is used.

    (a) 1/16
    (b) 1/8
    (c) 1/4
    (d) 1/2

29. _____ are appliances used in orthodontics to expand the palatal
    arch.

    (a) Activators
    (b) Bite planes
    (c) Retainers
    (d) Space maintainers

30. The ball retainer clasps of the Hawley retainer are placed _____
    between the first and second molars.

    (a) against the gingival papilla
    (b) in the embrasure
    (c) next to the embrasure
    (d) A and B

31. As the final finish, orthodontic study casts are _____.

    (a) etched
    (b) glazed
    (c) polished
    (d) A and B

32. Cephalometrics is the scientific system of measurement of the _____.

    (a) bones of the oral cavity.
    (b) bone length.
    (c) cranial bones.
    (d) maxillary and mandibular bones.

33. In the construction of a retainer, the cast is coated with _____ prior to the application of the acrylic.

    (a) liquid soap
    (b) polymer
    (c) separating medium
    (d) wax

34. After a stainless steel wire has been bent, it must be _____.

    (a) autoclaved
    (b) baked
    (c) cold-cured
    (d) heat treated

35. A/an _____ is a molded wire appliance that serves as the interconnection between the molar bands and the extraoral neck or head straps.

    (a) arch wire
    (b) Crozat
    (c) face bow
    (d) monobloc

PROCEDURE: PLACEMENT OF POSTERIOR ELASTIC ORTHODONTIC SEPARATORS

GOAL: The student will demonstrate the placement of posterior elastic orthodontic separators on a typodont.

SE = Student evaluation C = Criterion met IE = Instructor evaluation X = Criterion not met	SE	IE
1. **Instruments and Materials:** typodont, separating pliers, elastics, (optional - petroleum jelly).		
2. Placed elastic on beaks of pliers. Squeezed pliers handles without breaking elastic.		
3. Gently forced elastic through the contact. Maintained patient comfort and integrity of the gingival tissue.		
4. If tight contact, lubricated elastic with petroleum jelly and used a sawing motion to position separator.		
5. Determined that elastic circled contact area and was clear of occlusion.		
Comments:		

PROCEDURE: PLACEMENT AND LIGATION OF ARCH WIRES		
GOAL: The student will demonstrate placement and ligation of arch wires with ligature ties on a typodont.		
SE = Student evaluation C = Criterion met IE = Instructor evaluation X = Criterion not met	SE	IE
1. **Instruments and Materials:** banded typodont, preformed arch wire, preformed ligature tie wires, ligature tying pliers, ligature cutting pliers, ligature tucker, and Schure instrument.		
2. Placed preformed arch wire from the anterior portion of the mouth. Simultaneously placed both ends into the tube slot on the banded posterior molar in both right and left quadrants.		
3. Selected preformed ligature tie wire. Placed loop around the four extensions of the bracket for each band.		
4. Guided tie wire behind all four brackets and over the arch wire. Pulled firm.		
5. Pulled top wire down over the arch wire and across the bottom wire. Pulled bottom wire up over other wire.		
6. With middle finger resting on the bracket tips, guided ligature tie ends through beaks of ligature tying pliers. Secured wire ends on pliers.		
7. Opened handles slightly to pull ligature wire ends tight. Squeezed handles and turned pliers clockwise or counterclockwise to make twist 4 to 5 mm. in length.		
8. Cut to leave 3 to 5 mm pigtail. Used Schure instrument (or wire tucker instrument) to tuck cut wire into space around the brackets and under the arch wire toward the gingiva.		
9. Checked patient comfort. Crimped distal ends of arch wire.		

PROCEDURE: REMOVAL OF LIGATURE TIES AND ARCH WIRE		
GOAL: The student will demonstrate removal of ligature ties and arch wire on a typodont.		
SE = Student evaluation C = Criterion met IE = Instructor evaluation X = Criterion not met	SE	IE
1. **Instruments and Materials:** banded typodont with ligature ties and arch wire in place, hemostat, Schure instrument or scaler, and ligature cutting pliers.		
2. Lifted wire ties from arch wire and bracket with Schure instrument or scaler.		
3. Held ligature wire with hemostat. Cut tie wires with ligature cutters.		
4. Used hemostat to remove cut ligature wire from bracket.		
5. Checked brackets for complete removal of tie wires.		
6. Straightened crimp in posterior end of arch wire.		
7. Removed arch wire by pulling forward.		
8. Checked for patient comfort and tissue integrity.		
Comments:		

PROCEDURE: REMOVAL OF EXCESS CEMENT WITH ULTRASONIC SCALER		
GOAL: The student will use an ultrasonic scaler to remove excess cement on a typodont.		
SE = Student evaluation C = Criterion met IE = Instructor evaluation X = Criterion not met	SE	IE
1. **Instruments and Materials:** typodont with cement on teeth, ultrasonic unit, handpiece and blunted scaling tips.		
2. Placed blunted scaling tip into handpiece. Checked water flow, water pressure and air pressure.		
3. Obtained fulcrum and held handpiece in a pen grasp or modified pen grasp.		
4. Placed tip lightly against tooth at a 15° angle positioned toward the occlusal.		
5. Moved tip constantly by applying short vertical strokes where the cement was located.		
6. Removed all cement while maintaining patient comfort and tissue integrity.		
Comments:		

LEARNING GOALS

The student will be able to:

1. Describe the indications, and contraindications, for endodontic treatment.

2. Identify endodontic instruments and describe their use and care.

3. Describe the specialized diagnostic tests used in an endodontic examination.

4. Describe the steps in endodontic treatment and differentiate between chemical and mechanical debridement of the root canal.

5. Describe the technique for obtaining an endodontic culture.

6. Demonstrate measuring and placing stops on endodontic instruments.

7. Demonstrate pulp vitality testing.

8. Demonstrate irrigating the root canal.

EXERCISES

1. A _____ is used for removal of gross fragments of pulp and for the extirpation of the vital pulp.

   (a) broach
   (b) Gates-Glidden drill
   (c) rat-tail file
   (d) reamer

2. A/an _____ is used to obtain a culture of the root canal.

   (a) aspirating syringe
   (b) Lentulo spiral
   (c) sterile paper point
   (d) sterile cotton pellet

3. Following removal of the apex of the root during an apicoectomy, a retrofilling may be placed using a/an _____.

   (a) endodontic spreader
   (b) Lentulo spiral
   (c) Messing gun
   (d) B or C

The following questions are based on the instruments shown below.

4. This is an enlarged view of a _____.

    (a) barbed broach
    (b) file
    (c) reamer
    (d) smooth broach

5. This is an enlarged view of a _____.

    (a) barbed broach
    (b) file
    (c) reamer
    (d) smooth broach

6. This is an enlarged view of a _____.

    (a) barbed broach
    (b) file
    (c) reamer
    (d) smooth broach

7. The instrument shown in question # _____ is used to enlarge, shape and smooth the root canal.

    (a) 4
    (b) 5
    (c) 6
    (d) none of the above

8. The instrument shown in question # _____ is most effective when used in a twisting motion.

    (a) 4
    (b) 5
    (c) 6
    (d) none of the above

9. _____ refers to anything that is used within the root canal.

    (a) Intercanal
    (b) Intracanal
    (c) Introcanal
    (d) Introradicular

10. _____ is a diagnostic test that involves gently tapping the tooth to determine the extent of sensitivity.

    (a) Mobility
    (b) Palpation
    (c) Percussion
    (d) Transillumination

11. Failure to accurately determine the length of the tooth may lead to apical perforation and overfilling.

    (a) true
    (b) false

12. A stop is placed _____ to the long axis of the instrument.

    (a) at an oblique angle
    (b) at a right angle
    (c) distal
    (d) parallel

13. Before the trial point is placed into the canal, the tip is _____ slightly.

    (a) blunted
    (b) narrowed
    (c) sharpened
    (d) tapered

14. A/an _____ is the surgical excision of the apical portion of the tooth through a surgical opening made in the overlying bone and gingival tissues.

    (a) apicoectomy
    (b) incision and drainage
    (c) periapical curettage
    (d) resection

15. _____ debridement is the progressive elimination of organic and inorganic debris within the root canal through the use of instruments.

    (a) Chemical
    (b) Mechanical

16. Teeth with full crown restorations can be pulp tested by placing the tip of the pulp tester on the occlusal surface of the crown.

    (a) true
    (b) false

17. After being placed, the rubber dam may be disinfected with _____.

    (a) glutaraldehyde
    (b) hydrogen peroxide
    (c) sodium hypochlorite
    (d) A or B

18. A _____ endodontic culture will appear cloudy.

    (a) negative
    (b) positive

19. "Mouth holds" of warm salt water are used to _____.

    (a) assist in localization of the swelling.
    (b) encourage drainage following an apicoectomy.
    (c) force the exudate from an abscess.
    (d) prevent a change in the pH of the tissues.

20. A/an _____ is used at chairside to sterilize files, reamers and broaches.

    (a) dry heat sterilizer
    (b) endodontic kit
    (c) glass bead sterilizer
    (d) hot oil sterilizer

21. _____ points, also referred to as absorbent points, are available in assorted sizes to adapt to the length and shape of the canals being treated.

    (a) Cotton
    (b) Gutta percha
    (c) Paper
    (d) Silver

22. If the tooth responds favorably to cold stimulus, _____ is/are usually present.

    (a) acute pulpalgia
    (b) advanced necrosis
    (c) infection
    (d) pulp stones

23. Placing the pulp tester on a metallic restoration gives a more accurate reading.

    (a) true
    (b) false

24. _____ may be used to bleach a discolored nonvital tooth.

    (a) Hydrogen peroxide
    (b) Sodium hypochlorite
    (c) Sodium perborate
    (d) A and C

25. The slab and spatula used to mix the cement for the final filling of the root canal must be _____.

    (a) cold
    (b) non-metallic
    (c) sterile
    (d) B and C

PROCEDURE: OBTAINING A PULP VITALITY READING		
GOAL: The student will demonstrate obtaining a pulp vitality test reading for a patient (on a control tooth).		
SE = Student evaluation C = Criterion met IE = Instructor evaluation X = Criterion not met	SE	IE
1. **Instruments and Materials:** Vitalometer (pulp tester), cotton rolls, air syringe, mouth mirror, toothpaste and patient chart.		
2. Seated patient. Explained procedure to patient. Washed hands.		
3. Dried and isolated control tooth.		
4. Applied a small amount of toothpaste to tip of pulp tester. Set control at "0".		
5. Placed tip firmly on the control tooth. Avoided placing tip on a metallic restoration.		
6. Slowly moved the indicator upward until the patient responded to the stimulus. Recorded response.		
7. Set control at "0" and repeated process. Recorded second reading on patient's chart.		
Comments:		

PROCEDURE: PLACING STOPS ON ENDODONTIC INSTRUMENTS		
GOAL: The student will placed stops on broaches, reamers or files (at 21 mm). The student will also arrange the instruments, ready for use, in a banker's sponge.		
SE = Student evaluation C = Criterion met IE = Instructor evaluation X = Criterion not met	SE	IE
1. **Instruments and Materials:** assorted endodontic broaches, reamers and files, endodontic measuring gauge, stops, banker's sponge (with glass dish and disinfecting solution).		
2. Used measuring gauge to determine position of the stop.		
3. Placed stop at right angle to the long axis of the instrument at the predetermined position.		
4. Arranged instruments in the banker's sponge in order of their type and size.		
Comments:		

PROCEDURE: IRRIGATING AND DRYING THE PULP CHAMBER AND CANALS		
GOAL: The student will irrigate the canals alternately using sodium hypochlorite and hydrogen peroxide. Upon completion of the irrigation, the student will dry the canals. (This is to be demonstrated on an extracted tooth with the root canals opened and enlarged.)		
SE = Student evaluation C = Criterion met IE = Instructor evaluation X = Criterion not met	SE	IE
1. **Instruments and Materials:** 2 irrigating syringes, 2 dappen dishes, irrigating solutions (sodium hypochlorite and hydrogen peroxide), sterile gauze pads, sterile absorbent paper points and prepared tooth.		
2. Filled one syringe with sodium hypochlorite. Filled the other syringe with hydrogen peroxide. Placed needles on syringes.		
3. Inserted needle loosely into the canal. Ejected solution slowly into canal. Used gauze pad to catch excess solution.		
4. Used solutions alternately. Sodium hypochlorite was the last solution used.		
5. Used sterile absorbent paper points to gently dry canals.		
6. Avoided getting solution on hands or the area surrounding the tooth.		
Comments:		

LEARNING GOALS

The student will be able to:

1. List the indications and contraindications for fixed prosthodontics and describe the role of the dental laboratory technician in fixed prosthodontics.

2. Describe the types of crowns and crown preparations including: full, veneer, dowel, seven-eighths and three-quarter crowns.

3. Relate the steps in the construction of a dowel post and crown and in a core build-up.

4. Describe the components of a bridge and the functions of each.

5. Describe three methods used for gingival retraction. Demonstrate gingival retraction using the chemical method.

6. Describe the methods of obtaining a bite registration.

7. Describe the laboratory steps involved in the construction of a fixed bridge and a veneer crown.

8. Demonstrate the construction of a custom acrylic tray.

9. Demonstrate preparing impression materials including: polysulfide (rubber base), silicone and hydrocolloid.

10. Demonstrate the preparation of temporary coverage.

EXERCISES

1. Polysulfide impression materials are mixed on a _____.

    (a) chilled slab
    (b) glass slab
    (c) paper pad
    (d) teflon pad

2. The loaded hydrocolloid impression tray is placed in the tempering bath at _____ F.

    (a) 98.6°
    (b) 105°
    (c) 110°
    (d) 115°

3. _____ cement is used for cementation of temporary coverage.

   (a) EBA
   (b) Polycarboxylate
   (c) Zinc phosphate
   (d) ZOE

4. Temporary crown and bridge coverage may be constructed by placing a doughy mix of self-cure acrylic in a/an _____.

   (a) alginate impression.
   (b) aluminum crown.
   (c) polycarbonate crown.
   (d) stainless steel crown.

5. A/an _____ is a natural tooth that becomes the support for the replacement tooth or teeth.

   (a) abutment
   (b) dowel crown
   (c) pontic
   (d) solder joint

6. In a bite registration, the index side refers to the arch _____.

   (a) containing the prepared teeth.
   (b) opposite the one containing the prepared teeth.

7. _____ cement is used for the permanent cementation of a fixed bridge.

   (a) Polycarboxylate
   (b) Silicophosphate
   (c) Zinc phosphate
   (d) A, B or C

8. A die is used in the indirect laboratory technique for the construction of a crown.

   (a) true
   (b) false

9. A _____ may be necessary in a tooth broken down by extensive caries.

   (a) core build-up
   (b) custom post
   (c) dowel crown
   (d) porcelain veneer

10. When mixing elastomeric impression materials, the _____ material is mixed first.

   (a) heavy-bodied (tray)
   (b) light-bodied (syringe)

11. _____ impression materials adapt well to pin holes used in the pin retention technique.

   (a) Alginate
   (b) Hydrocolloid
   (c) Polysulfide
   (d) Silicone

12. When constructing a custom tray using the vacuum technique, _____ is placed over the cast to form a spacer.

   (a) acrylic
   (b) asbestos
   (c) styrofoam
   (d) wax

13. When waxing an indirect pattern, the first step is to _____.

   (a) heat the die.
   (b) lubricate the die with separating medium.
   (c) polish the die.
   (d) soak the die in cold water.

14. The mixing time for polysulfide impression material should not exceed _____.

   (a) 30 to 45 seconds
   (b) 45 to 60 seconds
   (c) 1 to 2 minutes
   (d) 2 to 3 minutes

15. When preparing hydrocolloid impression materials, the accelerator is stirred into the base material with a circular motion.

   (a) true
   (b) false

16. Heavy-bodied silicone putty may be used for the _____ impression.

   (a) preliminary
   (b) secondary

17. The ideal point for the attachment of the sprue pin is _____.

   (a) at the thickest part of the wax pattern.
   (b) away from the detailed occlusal anatomy.
   (c) positioned to provide access and flow of the molten metal.
   (d) A, B and C

18. _____ expansion is caused as a result of absorption of water.

   (a) Cristobalite
   (b) Hygroscopic
   (c) Investment
   (d) Thermal

19. _____ is the process that removes oxides on the metal casting.

   (a) Burnout
   (b) Pickling
   (c) Polishing
   (d) Spruing

20. The _____ contained in one type of retraction cord is potentially hazardous to the cardiovascular patient.

   (a) aluminum chloride
   (b) racemic epinephrine
   (c) tannic acid
   (d) zinc chloride

21. Fixed prosthodontics is _____ in the presence of periodontal disease or lack of vitality of the abutment.

   (a) contraindicated
   (b) indicated

22. Gingival retraction is performed _____.

   (a) after taking the preliminary impression.
   (b) before local anesthesia is administered.
   (c) prior to cutting the preparation.
   (d) prior to taking the final impression.

23. _____ is performed by using an electric loop or wire tip that is heated to an extremely high temperature.

   (a) Electric cautery
   (b) Electrosurgery
   (c) Hydrocautery
   (d) Mechanical retraction

24. Bite registration paste should be spatulated into a homogeneous mix within _____.

   (a) 15 seconds
   (b) 30 seconds
   (c) 45 seconds
   (d) 1 minute

25. Hydrocolloid impression material reaches a final set in the mouth in approximately _____ minutes.

   (a) 1 to 3
   (b) 3 to 5
   (c) 5 to 8
   (d) 8 to 10

26. A _____ crown preparation covers the entire coronal area of the posterior tooth with the exception of a portion of the mesiofacial surface near the occlusal.

   (a) full
   (b) 3/4
   (c) 7/8
   (d) veneer

27. The _____ displacement of tissue may be accomplished by placing a crown filled with gutta percha and eucalyptol over the prepared tooth.

    (a) chemical
    (b) mechanical
    (c) surgical
    (d) A and B

28. A/an _____ impression material may be used for impressions to construct an onlay and crown and bridge abutments or for a copper band impression of a single tooth.

    (a) alginate
    (b) hydrocolloid
    (c) polysulfide
    (d) zinc oxide-eugenol paste

29. The loaded hydrocolloid syringe is placed in the storage bath for _____.

    (a) 3 to 5 minutes
    (b) 5 to 10 minutes
    (c) 15 to 30 minutes
    (d) 24 hours

30. A temporary aluminum crown should extend no more than _____ mm. beyond the gingival margin of the tooth.

    (a) .02
    (b) .05
    (c) 1.0
    (d) 1.5

PROCEDURE: CONSTRUCTING A CUSTOM ACRYLIC IMPRESSION TRAY		
GOAL: The student will demonstrate the construction of a custom acrylic impression tray for the mandibular left quadrant.		
SE = Student evaluation C = Criterion met IE = Instructor evaluation X = Criterion not met	SE	IE
1. Instruments and Materials: cast of mandibular left quadrant, utility wax, baseplate wax (for spacer), wax spatula, warm water or bunsen burner to soften wax, tray resin and measuring devices, glass jar with lid or a paper cup, small spatula or wooden tongue blade, petroleum jelly.		
2. Filled undercuts on cast with utility wax.		
3. Shaped wax spacer (two thicknesses) over cast.		
4. Used wax spatula to cut stops in wax on nonprepared teeth.		
5. Mixed tray resin according to manufacturer's directions. Allowed mix to reach doughy stage.		
6. Lubricated palms of hands with petroleum jelly. Kneaded resin to form a thick patty.		
7. Shaped resin dough on cast to form tray and handle.		
8. Removed wax spacer from tray after resin reached initial set (7 to 10 minutes).		
9. Reseated tray on cast until acrylic was fully set.		
Comments:		

PROCEDURE: FINISHING A CUSTOM ACRYLIC IMPRESSION TRAY		
GOAL: The student will demonstrate finishing (smoothing and painting with adhesive) a custom acrylic impression tray.		
SE = Student evaluation C = Criterion met IE = Instructor evaluation X = Criterion not met	SE	IE
1. **Instruments and Materials:** unfinished custom tray and quadrant cast, safety goggles, acrylic burs, straight handpiece (SHP) and bench motor, lathe, rag wheel and pumice, and tray adhesive.		
2. Wore safety goggles.		
3. Used acrylic burs to smooth rough edges.		
4. Buffed and polished margins on lathe.		
5. <u>Optional:</u> Used #8 round acrylic bur to place perforations in tray.		
6. Coated inside of tray with manufacturer's tray adhesive.		
Comments:		

PROCEDURE: CONSTRUCTING ACRYLIC TEMPORARY COVERAGE		
GOAL: The student will demonstrate the construction of a temporary custom crown on a typodont.		
SE = Student evaluation C = Criterion met IE = Instructor evaluation X = Criterion not met	SE	IE
1. **Instruments and Materials:** typodont with prepared tooth, preliminary alginate impression (before the tooth was prepared), acrylic resin monomer and polymer, separating medium, spatula (small cement), small jar with lid, scissors, straight handpiece (SHP), finishing burs and disks, lathe, rag wheel, pumice and safety goggles.		
2. Mixed polymer and monomer following manufacturer's instructions. Allowed mix to reach doughy stage.		
3. Coated prepared tooth with separating medium.		
4. Placed resin dough in area of prepared tooth. Replaced impression in mouth for 3 minutes.		
5. Removed tray from patient's mouth. Removed temporary coverage from impression.		
6. Used scissors or sandpaper disks and burs to trim and finish temporary crown.		
7. Wore safety goggles. Used rag wheel on lathe for final polish.		
Comments:		

PROCEDURE: PLACEMENT AND REMOVAL OF RETRACTION CORD		
GOAL: The student will place, and remove, a length of chemically impregnated retraction cord around a prepared tooth (on a typodont).		
SE = Student evaluation C = Criterion met IE = Instructor evaluation X = Criterion not met	SE	IE
1. **Instruments and Materials:** Typodont with prepared tooth, retraction cord, cotton pliers, cotton rolls, air/water syringe, scissors, plastic instrument (blunted tip).		
2. Packed quadrant with cotton rolls and gently dried retraction site with warm air.		
3. Cut length (1 to 1 1/2 inches) of retraction cord.		
4. Picked up cord with cotton pliers. Twisted cord to tighten fibers. Started placement of cord at interproximal area.		
5. Used blunt plastic instrument to pack cord gently around the cervical area. Ends of cord overlapped slightly with one end extending between the teeth.		
6. Left cord in place for 5 to 10 minutes.		
7. Used cotton pliers to grasp tip of exposed end of cord. Removed cord in reverse sequence to the placement.		
8. Flushed area with warm water and dried with warm air.		
Comments:		

	SE	IE
PROCEDURE: MIXING POLYSULFIDE (RUBBER BASE) LIGHT-BODY (SYRINGE) IMPRESSION MATERIAL		
GOAL: The student will mix the impression material and load the syringe within the acceptable time limit. (Optional: materials may be used to take an impression on a typodont.)		
SE = Student evaluation C = Criterion met IE = Instructor evaluation X = Criterion not met		
1. Instruments and Materials: paper pad, spatula, rubber base syringe material (base and accelerator), syringe and tip, dappen dish, tissue and typodont (optional).		
2. Extruded equal lengths (1-1/4 to 2 inches) of base and accelerator on mixing pad. Replaced caps on tubes.		
3. Placed tip of spatula in the accelerator. Stirred the material into the base with a circular motion. Mixture fully spatulated (homogeneous mix) within 60 seconds.		
4. Used spatula to place bulk of material in dappen dish.		
5. Dipped sleeve of syringe into material and used plunger to draw the material up into the sleeve.		
6. Used tissue to clean end of sleeve. Placed tip device on end of syringe sleeve. Loading and assembly completed within 30 seconds.		
7. Put syringe aside while mixing tray material.		
Comments:		

PROCEDURE: MIXING POLYSULFIDE (RUBBER BASE) HEAVY-BODY (TRAY) IMPRESSION MATERIAL		
GOAL: The student will mix the impression material and load the tray within the acceptable time limit. (Optional: materials may be used to take an impression on a typodont.)		
SE = Student evaluation C = Criterion met IE = Instructor evaluation X = Criterion not met	SE	IE
1. Instruments and Materials: paper pad, spatula, rubber base heavy-bodied material (base and accelerator), custom tray and spacer material, and typodont (optional).		
2. Extruded equal lengths (length of liner plus 1/4 inch) of base and accelerator on mixing pad. Replaced caps on tubes.		
3. Placed tip of spatula in the accelerator. Stirred the material into the base with a circular motion. Mixture fully spatulated (homogeneous mix) within 60 seconds.		
4. Used spatula to load tray.		
5. Optional: Used syringe and tray material to take an impression on a typodont.		
6. Cleaned up all materials and returned to storage.		
Comments:		

LEARNING GOALS

The student will be able to:

1. Differentiate between fixed and removable prosthodontics and describe the role of the assistant and the laboratory technician in removable prosthodontics.

2. Describe the indications and contraindications for removable prosthodontics including intraoral and extraoral factors affecting the patient.

3. List the components of complete and partial dentures.

4. Describe the appointments and steps necessary for completion of a complete or partial denture.

5. Describe the construction of an overdenture and the different types of implants.

6. Demonstrate construction of a custom tray for a secondary impression.

EXERCISES

1. The components of a removable partial denture include a _____.

   (a) bar
   (b) framework
   (c) saddle
   (d) A, B and C

2. Akers, circumferential and Roach are types of _____.

   (a) attachments
   (b) bars
   (c) clasps
   (d) rests

3. Anterior denture teeth are held in place by gold pins that extend into the acrylic.

   (a) true
   (b) false

4. A removable partial denture designed with a connector and attachments can serve as a/an _____.

    (a) cingulum support
    (b) occlusal rest
    (c) splint
    (d) stress-breaker

5. The _____ of a removable partial denture is/are designed to control the extent of the "seating" of the prosthesis.

    (a) bar
    (b) clasps
    (c) rests
    (d) A and B

6. Occlusal bite rims register _____ and occlusal relationship of the mandibular and maxillary arches.

    (a) lateral excursion
    (b) muscle trim
    (c) protrusive dimension
    (d) vertical dimension

7. The posterior palatal seal is commonly referred to as the _____.

    (a) occlusive seal
    (b) palatal rugae
    (c) post-dam
    (d) posterior margin

8. During the secondary impression procedure the patient is directed to make facial and swallowing movements. This step is called _____.

    (a) bite registration
    (b) Gothic arch tracing
    (c) muscle trimming
    (d) occlusal equilibration

9. Artificial denture teeth are selected according to _____, shade and material.

    (a) color
    (b) mold
    (c) shape
    (d) size

10. The _____ technique of bite registration uses the patient's ability to create his or her own occlusal relationship by tracing, in wax, the movements of the mandible on the maxilla.

    (a) functionally generated path
    (b) Gothic arch tracing
    (c) occlusal relationship
    (d) wax tracing

11. A _____ removable denture receives all its retention and support from the underlying tissues.

    (a) full
    (b) partial

12. An immediate denture refers to a denture that is constructed and delivered following the extraction of the _____ teeth.

    (a) anterior
    (b) posterior
    (c) remaining
    (d) A and B

13. A surgical template is used to aid the surgeon in _____.

    (a) contouring the remaining alveolar ridge.
    (b) extracting the remaining teeth.
    (c) placing the immediate denture.
    (d) suturing the mucosa into place.

14. A _____ is/are used in producing a Gothic arch tracing.

    (a) stylus
    (b) tracing table
    (c) wax bite
    (d) A and B

15. A/an _____ is a complete denture supported by the bony ridge, the mucosa, and a few remaining natural teeth.

    (a) fixed bridge
    (b) overdenture
    (c) removable bridge
    (d) unilateral denture

16. Because of resorption of the alveolar ridge, an immediate denture usually must be _____ within 3 to 6 months following surgery.

    (a) duplicated
    (b) relined
    (c) repaired
    (d) replaced

17. A/an _____ implant is surgically placed onto the alveolus.

    (a) blade
    (b) endosseous
    (c) subperiosteal
    (d) tripod

18. The _____ of a mandibular partial denture extends from the retromolar area lingually to the mylohyoid ridge and facially to the oblique ridge.

    (a) connector
    (b) flange
    (c) framework
    (d) saddle

19. _____ may be used to take the secondary impression for a partial denture.

    (a) Alginate
    (b) Elastomeric impression material
    (c) Zinc oxide-eugenol impression paste
    (d) B or C

20. _____ posterior denture teeth are modified to reduce the effects and pressures of occlusion that are transmitted through the denture to the oral mucosa and the residual alveolar ridge.

    (a) Anatomic
    (b) Nonanatomic

21. A/an _____ is used for making bite relationship records, for arranging artificial teeth, and for trial placement in the mouth.

    (a) baseplate
    (b) bite rim
    (c) occlusal rim
    (d) occlusal plate

22. During the try-in the patient is asked to swallow, yawn and to verbalize certain sounds. This is done to check the _____.

    (a) extension of the flange.
    (b) occlusal relationship.
    (c) retention of the denture.
    (d) vertical dimension.

23. _____ artificial teeth have a tendency to wear under occlusion; however, they do not produce a clicking sound during mastication.

    (a) Acrylic
    (b) Porcelain
    (c) Slot
    (d) Tube

24. A _____ minute appointment is usually adequate for delivery of a partial denture.

    (a) 10 to 15
    (b) 15 to 20
    (c) 20 to 30
    (d) 30 to 45

25. For an immediate denture patient, sutures are usually removed _____ after surgery.

    (a) 24 hours
    (b) 24 to 48 hours
    (c) 48 to 72 hours
    (d) 7 days

26. A/an _____ involves a tooth that is endodontically treated and with the tooth structure greatly reduced.

    (a) endosseous implant
    (b) long coping
    (c) short coping
    (d) subperiosteal implant

27. Anterior teeth with single short roots usually _____ provide adequate stability to support a removable partial prosthesis.

    (a) do
    (b) do not

The following questions are based on the figure shown below.

28. This is a lingual _____.

   (a) bar
   (b) connector
   (c) rest
   (d) saddle

29. This _____ is placed on the mesial of the premolar.

   (a) clasp
   (b) flange
   (c) onlay
   (d) rest

30. This is hinged and is used to _____.

   (a) facilitate cleaning.
   (b) relieve stress.
   (c) seat the appliance.
   (d) splint the teeth.

31. This _____ extends back over the retromolar area.

   (a) baseplate
   (b) bite rim
   (c) framework
   (d) saddle

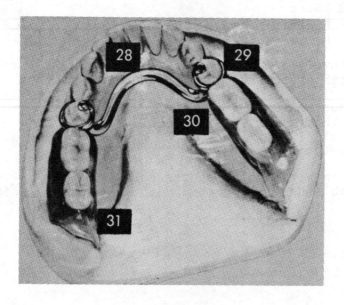

32. _____ is the carving of baseplate material to simulate normal tissue contours, grooves and eminences.

    (a) Contouring
    (b) Festooning
    (c) Milling
    (d) Stippling

33. _____ are excluded on dentures to provide an accurate fit of the denture and to provide space in the posterior region for the patient to close, swallow, speak and masticate.

    (a) First molars
    (b) Posterior teeth
    (c) Premolars
    (d) Third molars

34. The laboratory technician follows the dentist's written prescription in the fabrication of the prosthesis.

    (a) true
    (b) false

35. A/an _____ is used to establish the design of the prosthesis and the path of insertion.

    (a) articulator
    (b) functional path bite registration
    (c) Gothic arch tracing
    (d) surveyor

PROCEDURE: MAKING A CUSTOM IMPRESSION TRAY (FOR A COMPLETE DENTURE)		
GOAL: The student will construct an impression tray for an edentulous maxillary or mandibular arch.		
SE = Student evaluation C = Criterion met IE = Instructor evaluation X = Criterion not met	SE	IE
1. Instruments and Materials: pencil, cast of edentulous arch, baseplate wax for spacer, wax carver, tray material and measuring devices, mixing container, block and roller, laboratory burs and straight handpiece and manufacturer's tray adhesive.		
2. Outlined the tray on the cast.		
3. Adapted wax to cast to provide spacer. Cut holes in the spacer for stops.		
4. Mixed tray material following manufacturer's instructions within 30 seconds. Allowed to stand until doughy and not sticky (2 to 3 minutes).		
5. Placed dough on block and rolled into sheet of uniform thickness.		
6. Adapted sheet of material over wax-covered cast and formed handle in anterior.		
7. Allowed tray to harden (7 to 10 minutes). Removed tray from cast and stripped out wax.		
8. Removed all remaining wax. Used laboratory bur in straight handpiece to smooth rough edges.		
9. Applied thin coating of adhesive.		
Comments:		

LEARNING GOALS

The student will be able to:

1. State the indications and contraindications for periodontal
   treatment and describe the role of the hygienist and assistant
   in periodontics.

2. Identify the instruments used in periodontics and describe the
   care of these instruments.

3. Describe the steps and procedures involved in a periodontal
   examination and demonstrate recording the patient's periodontal
   conditions as dictated by the periodontist.

4. Describe the specialized periodontal procedures including
   prophylaxis, scaling and curettage, root planing, gingivectomy,
   gingivoplasty and osteoplasty.

5. Demonstrate mixing eugenol-type and non-eugenol-type periodontal
   surgical dressings.

EXERCISES

1. A periodontal pocket probe is used to _____.

   (a) mark periodontal pockets.
   (b) measure the depth of the sulcus.
   (c) surgically remove periodontal pockets.
   (d) A and C

2. A _____ has a single straight cutting edge and is designed to
   remove gross supra- and subgingival calculus on the posterior
   teeth.

   (a) chisel
   (b) file scaler
   (c) hoe scaler
   (d) surgical hoe

3. The ultrasonic scaling unit is used in a prophylaxis to remove
   _____ from the gingival area of the crown.

   (a) cauterized tissue
   (b) deposits
   (c) hypertrophied tissue
   (d) stains

4. _____ is the process of cleansing an area or a pocket and removing the necrotic tissue in the area.

   (a) Curettage
   (b) Planing
   (c) Prophylaxis
   (d) Scaling

5. A/an _____ is the surgical reshaping of the gingivae and papillae for correction of deformities and to restore the gingivae to a normal functional form.

   (a) frenectomy
   (b) gingivectomy
   (c) gingivoplasty
   (d) osteoplasty

6. _____ are designed for interdental tissue removal in a gingivectomy procedure.

   (a) Electrosurgery tips
   (b) Interdental knives
   (c) Rotary scalers
   (d) Ultrasonic knives

7. Tooth mobility recorded as a 2 (or II) indicates _____ mobility.

   (a) extreme
   (b) moderate
   (c) normal
   (d) slight

8. A periodontal flap involves the total removal of a section of gingival tissue from a donor site.

   (a) true
   (b) false

9. A/an _____ periodontal pocket involves the alveolar bone as one wall of the pocket area.

   (a) infra-bony
   (b) supra-bony

10. The dental plaque index uses the number 3 to indicate _____.

    (a) minimal plaque.
    (b) no plaque.
    (c) plaque covering less than one third of the tooth surface.
    (d) plaque covering more than one half of the tooth surface.

11. _____ involves the mechanical removal of calculus, debris, plaque and stains on the coronal surfaces of the teeth and in the gingival sulcus.

    (a) Coronal polishing
    (b) Curettage
    (c) Prophylaxis
    (d) Root planing

12. Teeth that are sensitive where the cementoenamel junction is exposed following surgery may be treated with _____.

    (a) a 2 per cent sodium fluoride and water solution.
    (b) specifically formulated commercial dentifrices.
    (c) topical anesthetics to numb the tissues.
    (d) A or B

13. A/an _____ is the surgical removal of diseased gingiva to eliminate periodontal pockets.

    (a) apicoectomy
    (b) curettage
    (c) gingivectomy
    (d) osteoplasty

14. _____ type periodontal dressings are used to protect a surgical site.

    (a) Calcium hydroxide
    (b) Eugenol
    (c) Non-eugenol
    (d) B and C

15. Poor general or mental health of the patient is a/an _____ for periodontal treatment.

    (a) contraindication
    (b) indication

16. A _____ has a continuous cutting edge with a rounded toe. It is
    the standard instrument for subgingival scaling and root
    planing.

    (a) curette
    (b) file scaler
    (c) Jaquette scaler
    (d) porte polisher

17. When the depth of the sulcus is greater than _____ mm., it is
    considered to be a periodontal pocket.

    (a) 2
    (b) 3
    (c) 4
    (d) 5

18. When charting the periodontal condition, a _____ pencil may be
    used to make a line on the chart to represent the patient's
    gingival crest.

    (a) blue
    (b) black
    (c) red
    (d) A, B or C

19. Periodontal surgical dressing is placed first on the _____
    surfaces and pressed gently onto the interproximal material to
    assure retention of the total dressing material.

    (a) distal
    (b) facial
    (c) lingual
    (d) mesial

20. A/an _____ is used to gently pry the mass of periodontal
    surgical dressing loose from the tissue.

    (a) explorer
    (b) interdental knife
    (c) scalpel
    (d) spoon excavator

21. The rubber tip for interdental cleansing is placed _____ into the interdental space.

    (a) at a right angle
    (b) horizontally
    (c) obliquely
    (d) vertically

22. Periodontal instruments may be cleaned by _____.

    (a) boiling water
    (b) disinfection
    (c) sterilization
    (d) B or C

23. Breakdown and fuzziness in the continuity of the lamina dura visible on the radiograph may indicate early signs of _____.

    (a) ANUG
    (b) gingivitis
    (c) pericoronitis
    (d) periodontitis

24. If hemorrhaging is acute during scaling and curettage, gauze squares soaked with _____ may be used momentarily as compresses to keep the area clean.

    (a) alcohol
    (b) eugenol
    (c) hemostatic agents
    (d) hydrogen peroxide mix

25. Following the placement of a periodontal surgical dressing the patient is advised to drink _____ fluids during the first 24 hours.

    (a) cold
    (b) hot

PROCEDURE: MIXING EUGENOL-TYPE PERIODONTAL DRESSING

GOAL: The student will mix and prepare for use eugenol-type periodontal dressing.

SE = Student evaluation C = Criterion met IE = Instructor evaluation X = Criterion not met	SE	IE
1. **Instruments and Materials:** eugenol-type dressing (powder and liquid), paper pad, spatula with a stiff blade, disposable gloves, oil of orange and plastic wrap.		
2. Put on plastic gloves. Placed materials on paper pad. (10 to 12 drops of liquid and 1 teaspoon of powder.)		
3. Incorporated liquid into powder to form a thick, putty-like mass.		
4. Kneaded mass with the palm and fingers and added more powder until mass would no longer take up powder.		
5. Formed the dressing into a rope approximately 4 to 5 mm. in diameter and 1 to 1-1/2 inches in length.		
6. Covered rope with powder and then placed securely in plastic wrap.		
7. Cleaned instruments and work area. Returned instruments and materials to storage.		
Comments:		

PROCEDURE: MIXING NON-EUGENOL-TYPE PERIODONTAL DRESSING		
GOAL: The student will mix and prepare for use non-eugenol-type periodontal dressing.		
SE = Student evaluation C = Criterion met IE = Instructor evaluation X = Criterion not met	SE	IE
1. **Instruments and Materials:** non-eugenol-type dressing (tubes of paste), paper pad, spatula with a stiff blade, disposable gloves, petroleum jelly, oil of orange and plastic wrap.		
2. Put on plastic gloves. Extruded equal lengths of catalyst and base (approximately 2 inches) on mixing pad.		
3. Used the spatula to quickly fold and mix the materials until evenly blended.		
4. Wiped spatula immediately, before dressing hardened on the blade.		
5. Coated gloved fingers with petroleum jelly. Formed ropes of dressing mix.		
6. Wrapped ropes in plastic wrap. Completed preparation within working time of 3 to 4 minutes.		
7. Cleaned instruments and work area. Returned instruments and materials to storage.		
Comments:		

LEARNING GOALS

The student will be able to:

1. Describe the indications and contraindications for oral surgery.

2. Name and state the uses of the specialized oral surgery instruments.

3. Describe the chain of asepsis and the assistant's role in oral surgery.

4. Describe oral surgery procedures including forceps extractions, alveolectomy and biopsy.

5. Demonstrate preparing sutures in the suture needle and removing sutures from the surgical site.

6. Discuss the assistant's role in hospital dentistry.

7. Demonstrate preparation of a sterile field for oral surgery instruments.

EXERCISES

1. During an extraction, a tooth is _____ in the socket to compress the bone and enlarge the socket.

   (a) aspirated
   (b) elevated
   (c) luxated
   (d) rotated

2. The #151 Cryer universal forceps is designed for the extraction of maxillary posterior teeth.

   (a) true
   (b) false

3. _____ is commonly known as "dry socket."

   (a) Alveolar osteitis
   (b) Alveolectomy
   (c) Alveolitis
   (d) A or C

4. _____ are a scissors-type of surgical instrument that have a spring between the handles and sharpened edges on the blade.

   (a) Elevators
   (b) Forceps
   (c) Hemostats
   (d) Rongeurs

5. In reference to dental forceps, the term _____ implies that one may be used either on the left or right side of one dental arch or that it may be used on either the maxillary or mandibular arch.

   (a) bilateral
   (b) multipurpose
   (c) unilateral
   (d) universal

6. In an _____ biopsy the entire lesion mass is excised, and the adjacent and underlying normal tissue is removed.

   (a) excision
   (b) exfoliative
   (c) exploratory
   (d) incision

7. After an extraction, a pressure pack made of sterile _____ is placed over the socket.

   (a) cotton rolls
   (b) gauze pads
   (c) hemostatic gauze
   (d) A or B

8. The antibiotic _____ may cause gastrointestinal disturbances in some patients.

   (a) ampicillin
   (b) erythromycin
   (c) penicillin
   (d) tetracycline

9. A paste dressing of _____ may be used to treat a dry socket.

   (a) calcium hydroxide
   (b) hydrogen peroxide
   (c) non-eugenol paste
   (d) zinc oxide-eugenol

10. A _____ is an elongated bundle of surgical gauze securely tied and with a long string attachment.

    (a) mouth prop
    (b) pressure pack
    (c) tongue guard
    (d) throat pack

11. An extraction is _____ when an active infection is present.

    (a) contraindicated
    (b) indicated

12. A/an _____ is a sharp instrument used with a push-pull action to remove sharp bone fragments.

    (a) apical elevator
    (b) bone file
    (c) chisel
    (d) curette

13. Surgical burs are made for both straight and contra-angle handpieces.

    (a) true
    (b) false

14. _____ forceps (No. 16) are designed to reach into the bifurcation of the roots of the mandibular molars.

    (a) Bayonet
    (b) Cowhorn
    (c) Curved
    (d) Universal

15. Because the surgical aspirating tip has such a small opening (aperture), a/an _____ may be needed to keep it open during use and to clean it prior to sterilization.

    (a) aspirator brush
    (b) hemostat
    (c) stylet
    (d) A and C

16. Before using the forceps to extract a tooth, the surgeon uses a/an _____ to loosen the gingival tissue and compress the alveolar bone.

    (a) apical elevator
    (b) bone compressor
    (c) gingival retractor
    (d) periosteal elevator

17. As a rule, if a scalpel has been used, _____ will be needed.

    (a) elevators
    (b) retractors
    (c) rongeurs
    (d) sutures

18. The threaded suture needle is placed _____ in the hemostat.

    (a) at an oblique angle
    (b) at a right angle
    (c) in the position of use
    (d) parallel

19. The hospital usually maintains a complete complement of dental equipment and instruments.

    (a) true
    (b) false

20. Surgical scrub involves scrubbing the hands with a disposable brush and an approved soap solution for _____ minutes.

    (a) 3
    (b) 5
    (c) 10
    (d) 15

21. External heat may be applied to the surgical area _____ to promote healing.

    (a) after the first 24 hours
    (b) during the first 24 hours

22. Prior to surgery, the assistant scrubs _____ she performs her preparatory duties.

    (a) after
    (b) before

23. A/an _____ is the surgical reduction or reshaping of the remaining alveolar ridge.

    (a) alveolectomy
    (b) exodontoectomy
    (c) frenectomy
    (d) osteotomy

24. The formation of regenerative bone may be detected in the radiograph within _____ following surgery.

    (a) 24 hours
    (b) 7 days
    (c) 6 to 8 weeks
    (d) 2 to 6 months

25. The tip of the _____ is designed to be placed at the crown of an impacted tooth or fractured crown.

    (a) apical elevator
    (b) Cryer forceps
    (c) periosteotome
    (d) tooth elevator

PROCEDURE: PREPARING SURGICAL INSTRUMENTS ON A STERILE FIELD		
GOAL: The student will demonstrate preparation of surgical instruments on a sterile field.		
SE = Student evaluation C = Criterion met IE = Instructor evaluation X = Criterion not met	SE	IE
1. Instruments and Materials: sterile towels, sterile oral surgery instruments, sterile transfer forceps.		
2. Washed hands.		
3. Opened sterile towel and placed it so that the outer surface was down (against the tray).		
3. Used sterile transfer forceps to place sterile instruments on inside of towel. Arranged instruments in order of use.		
4. When all instruments were in place, opened a second sterile towel. Placed this towel so the inner surface covered the instruments.		
5. Washed hands again (surgical scrub) before assisting with surgery.		
Comments:		

PROCEDURE: SUTURE REMOVAL		
GOAL: The student will demonstrate simulated suture removal on a manikin or typodont.		
SE = Student evaluation C = Criterion met IE = Instructor evaluation X = Criterion not met	SE	IE
1. **Instruments and Materials:** model with simulated suture placement, cotton swab, disinfecting solution, sterile gauze squares, cotton pliers, suture scissors, patient's chart.		
2. Washed hands and explained procedure to patient.		
3. Disinfected suture area. Blotted area with sterile gauze squares.		
4. Grasped suture knot in cotton pliers and pulled gently away from tissue.		
5. Gently placed the blade of the suture scissors under the suture and cut it.		
6. Using cotton pliers to hold the knot. Gently pulled the suture out of tissue. (Avoided pulling the knot through the tissue.)		
7. Repeated step until all sutures were removed.		
8. Counted number of sutures removed, checked against number noted on patient's chart at time of placement. Noted on patient's chart the number of sutures removed.		
Comments:		

CHAPTER 30   THE ADMINISTRATIVE ASSISTANT

LEARNING GOALS

The student will be able to:

1. Describe how the term "marketing" is applied in dentistry.

2. Demonstrate answering the telephone and greeting patients in a professional manner.

3. List the four criteria for all appointment book entries and the four elements to be included in outlining the appointment book.

4. Identify the following: units of time, buffer time, cancellation or call list, and a daily schedule sheet.

5. Describe how to schedule appointments for the following: an appointment series, children, new patients, recall patients, emergency patients and appointments utilizing an EFDA.

6. Identify and show how to use each of the following filing systems: alphabetical, numerical, cross-reference, chronological and subject.

7. Write an acceptable business letter in either block or modified block style.

8. Describe several recall systems and discuss the comparative merits of each.

EXERCISES

1. A patient finishes treatment in August. With a six-month recall period he should be seen again in _____.

   (a) December
   (b) February
   (c) January
   (d) March

2. A/an _____ file is a listing to enable one to locate materials filed under the numerical filing system.

   (a) alphabetical
   (b) chronological
   (c) cross-reference
   (d) tickler

3. Recall patients are usually scheduled directly with the _____.

   (a) dental health educator
   (b) dentist
   (c) EFDA
   (d) hygienist

4. Dental charts (the patient's clinical records) should be kept on file _____.

   (a) until the patient completes treatment.
   (b) three years after his last visit.
   (c) at least 10 years.
   (d) forever.

5. A _____ patient should be asked to come to the dental office at least 15 minutes before the beginning of their appointment.

   (a) child
   (b) geriatric
   (c) new
   (d) recall

6. In the _____ recall system the patient is sent more than one reminder notice.

   (a) advance appointment
   (b) instant
   (c) multiple copy
   (d) ongoing

7. The dentist will usually speak to _____ when they telephone.

   (a) other professionals
   (b) new patients
   (c) stock brokers
   (d) A and B

8. Most practices work on a _____ minute time unit because it provides scheduling flexibility.

   (a) 5
   (b) 10
   (c) 15
   (d) 20

9. With good appointment control _____.

   (a) patients are seen on time.
   (b) the dentist and staff make effective use of their time.
   (c) the patient load is well balanced.
   (d) A, B and C

10. In a business letter, the reference initials are placed _____ the "carbon copies" entry.

   (a) above
   (b) below

11. _____ is the arrangement of captions and indexing units in strict alphabetical order.

   (a) Alphabetizing
   (b) Captioning
   (c) Filing
   (d) Indexing

12. Insurance claim forms should be stored as part of the patient's chart.

   (a) true
   (b) false

13. On the daily schedule, a _____ next to the patient's name indicates that the appointment has been confirmed.

   (a) check-mark
   (b) circle

14. When filing alphabetically, terms denoting seniority (such as "Senior and "Junior") are _____.

   (a) captions
   (b) for information only
   (c) Unit 4 indexing units
   (d) A and C

15. In a _____ letter, all parts of the letter are blocked against the left margin.

   (a) block style
   (b) business style
   (c) modified-block style
   (d) semi-block style

16. _____ are used to make it easier to sort records into active and inactive files.

    (a) File guides
    (b) Index cards
    (c) Outguides
    (d) Purge tabs

17. A/an _____ is a bookmark for the filing system.

    (a) aging tab
    (b) drawer label
    (c) file guide
    (d) outguide

18. The name and title of the person sending the letter should always be typed under the signature, even if they are printed as part of the letterhead.

    (a) true
    (b) false

19. _____ encompasses all activities involved in attracting and retaining satisfied patients in the practice.

    (a) Advertising
    (b) Community outreach
    (c) Marketing
    (d) Patient education

20. It is courteous to permit the person _____ the call to hang up first.

    (a) originating
    (b) receiving

21. The appointment book entry is made _____ the appointment card is completed.

    (a) after
    (b) before

22. When scheduling with an EFDA, a dark bar on the left side of the appointment column indicates time when the _____ is with the patient.

    (a) dentist
    (b) EFDA
    (c) hygienist
    (d) B and C

23. A/an _____ period is scheduled each day to handle emergency patients.

    (a) buffer
    (b) emergency
    (c) matrix
    (d) overflow

24. All appointment book entries are made in ink.

    (a) true
    (b) false

25. A broken appointment should be recorded on the _____.

    (a) account ledger card
    (b) daily schedule
    (c) patient's chart
    (d) no-show list

PROCEDURE: ANSWERING THE TELEPHONE IN A PROFESSIONAL MANNER		
GOAL: In a classroom simulation, the student will demonstrate answering the telephone in a manner appropriate for a professional office.		
SE = Student evaluation C = Criterion met IE = Instructor evaluation X = Criterion not met	SE	IE
1. Answered telephone promptly on first or second ring.		
2. Greeted caller pleasantly.		
3. Clearly identified office and self.		
4. Offered to assist the caller.		
5. Either handled the call completely or took an appropriate message.		
6. Terminated conversation pleasantly.		
Comments:		

PROCEDURE: WRITING A BUSINESS LETTER		
GOAL: The student will write an acceptable business letter using full-block style using the information shown below. The letter is addressed to: Jamestown Dental Supply Co., 2020 Stapleton Drive, Anytown, MI 07924. In the letter request information about the new "Superfine" dental handpiece which they advertised in this month's dental journal. You are requesting this information for your employer.		
SE = Student evaluation C = Criterion met IE = Instructor evaluation X = Criterion not met	SE	IE
1. The letter was neat in appearance. (If typewritten, it was free of strikeovers, errors or erasures. If handwritten, it was legible, free of smudges, erasures, cross-outs or errors.)		
2. All components of a business letter were present and in proper location for a full-block style letter. (Heading, date, inside address, salutation, body of letter, complimentary close, signature, reference initials.)		
3. The body of the letter was easy to read and clearly stated the purpose of the letter.		
Comments:		

LEARNING GOALS

The student will be able to:

1. Differentiate between earnings and income and describe how these affect all dental health team members.

2. List the three major places where fee information is recorded.

3. Differentiate between a computerized service bureau and an in-house computer system.

4. Describe the proper management of payments received.

5. List the four basic office policies which are part of good preventive account control.

6. Describe the role of the administrative assistant in making financial arrangements and state when such arrangements should be made.

7. Describe the four most common payment plans offered in the dental office.

8. Differentiate between non-itemized, semi-itemized and itemized statements.

9. Describe the role of the collection agency in collecting overdue accounts.

10. Demonstrate making a pegboard accounting entry to record treatment provided, fees charged, payment received, and the balance owed.

EXERCISES

1. A/an _____ is a company with a central computer that provides service to many dental offices.

   (a) billing service
   (b) in-house computer
   (c) management bureau
   (d) service bureau

2. _____ is/are made up of payments actually received.

   (a) Fees
   (b) Earnings
   (c) Income
   (d) Overhead

3. When telephoning about an overdue account, you must always make sure that you are talking to the _____.

   (a) head of the household
   (b) husband
   (c) person responsible for the account
   (d) spouse

4. A/an _____ statement lists only the total amount due.

   (a) computerized
   (b) itemized
   (c) non-itemized
   (d) semi-itemized

5. The fee that the bank charges for handling credit card transactions is called _____.

   (a) debiting
   (b) discounting
   (c) pro-rating
   (d) rebating

6. An in-house computerized system requires _____ to safeguard data.

   (a) backup
   (b) database updates
   (c) print-outs
   (d) B and C

7. Under the _____ law it is illegal for anyone to use false pretenses to get information.

   (a) Federal Equal Credit Opportunity Act
   (b) Federal Fair Credit Reporting Act
   (c) Federal Fair Debt Collection Practice Act
   (d) Federal Truth in Lending Act

8. A/an _____ is helpful in tracking, and taking action on, overdue accounts.

   (a) accounts receivable report
   (b) credit report
   (c) daily journal
   (d) proof of posting

9. Pegboard accounting is one form of double entry bookkeeping.

    (a) true
    (b) false

10. _____ are used to transmit fee information from the treatment area to the business office.

    (a) Charge slips
    (b) Input documents
    (c) Walk-out statements
    (d) A and C

11. The _____ is a record that shows charges, payments and balances owed by each patient or family.

    (a) chart
    (b) ledger card
    (c) journal
    (d) statement

12. In _____ billing, the alphabet is divided into parts, and statements for each part of the alphabet are mailed at specified times during the month.

    (a) computer
    (b) cycle
    (c) pegboard
    (d) semi-itemized

13. A/an _____ provides a financial "x-ray" of the patient.

    (a) collection agency
    (b) credit report
    (c) itemized statement
    (d) patient registration form

14. Financial arrangements should be made with patients _____.

    (a) at the conclusion of treatment.
    (b) before 30 days.
    (c) prior to treatment.
    (d) upon request from the patient.

15. Which of the following is/are collection options for handling overdue accounts.

    (a) collection agency
    (b) credit bureau
    (c) small claims court
    (d) A and C

16. _____ represent all charges, payments and outstanding balances owed to the practice.

    (a) Accounts payable
    (b) Accounts receivable
    (c) Proof of posting
    (d) A and C

17. The amount of the _____ must match the amount of receipts.

    (a) bank deposit
    (b) cash fund
    (c) charge slips
    (d) walk-out statements

18. If there is a finance charge or a written agreement that specifies more than four payments it is necessary to complete a _____.

    (a) budget plan contract
    (b) Federal Truth in Lending form
    (c) financial agreement
    (d) A and C

19. All payments must be entered on the _____.

    (a) account ledger card
    (b) daily journal page
    (c) receivables report
    (d) A and B

20. As part of proof of posting, the total receipts must match the money in the cash drawer minus _____.

    (a) credit card slips
    (b) outstanding balances
    (c) the change fund
    (d) B and C

21. It is better to have the patient make small regular payments as planned than to have him frequently miss, or be late with, larger payments.

    (a) true
    (b) false

22. It is legal to telephone a debtor between the hours of _____.

    (a) 6 to 8 a.m.
    (b) 5 to 8 p.m.
    (c) 9 to 11 p.m.
    (d) it is never legal to telephone a debtor

23. An accounts receivable report _____ be generated with a pegboard system.

    (a) can
    (b) cannot

24. The patient has a previous balance of $50. Today's charges were $45 and the patient made a payment by check of $30. The balance on this account is _____.

    (a) $45
    (b) $55
    (c) $65
    (d) $95

25. When the patient makes a payment by credit card, the amount of the bank's service charge is subtracted from the patient's account.

    (a) true
    (b) false

PROCEDURE: MAKING PEGBOARD ACCOUNTING ENTRIES		
GOAL: The student will make a pegboard entry for the following transactions. John Jones was the patient. Mr. Jones had no previous balance. Today the dentist performed an examination and completed two two-surfaced amalgam restorations. The total fee was $65 and Mr. Jones made a cash payment of $40.		

SE = Student evaluation C = Criterion met IE = Instructor evaluation X = Criterion not met	SE	IE
1. **Instruments and Materials:** pegboard (or a simulation), daily journal page, account ledger card, charge/receipt slip and a pen.		
2. Completed charge slip entry. (Patient's name and notation concerning previous balance.)		
3. Made all other entries for today's visit. (Date, treatment codes, charges, payment and new balance.)		
4. Gave patient a receipt for the cash payment.		
Comments:		

LEARNING GOALS

The student will be able to:

1. Identify the major types of dental health care programs.

2. Identify the factors which affect coverage differences and describe the two major methods of payment.

3. Discuss ways of determining eligibility.

4. Differentiate between a pre-treatment estimate and a claim for payment.

5. Correctly use the terminology associated with dental insurance.

6. Demonstrate completing an insurance claim form.

EXERCISES

1. The patient signs a/an _____ form giving the dentist permission to send information concerning his treatment to the insurance company.

   (a) attending dentist's statement
   (b) assignment
   (c) authorization
   (d) release of information

2. A _____ is an example of a not-for-profit organization offering dental insurance coverage.

   (a) closed panel
   (b) Delta Dental Plan
   (c) Health Maintenance Organization
   (d) Preferred Provider Organization

3. _____ is the subscriber's signature telling the insurance carrier that he wants the benefits to be paid directly to the dentist and not to himself.

   (a) Assignment of benefits
   (b) Predetermination of benefits
   (c) Release of information
   (d) Schedule of allowances

4. Government programs usually provide their clients with some form of proof of eligibility. It is necessary to check this information _____.

   (a) after the patient is examined.
   (b) at each visit.
   (c) before each recall visit.
   (d) upon completion of treatment.

5. _____ is a fixed amount paid per patient each month that entitles him or her to prescribed benefits.

   (a) Capitation
   (b) CHAMPUS
   (c) Preferred Provider Organization
   (d) Schedule of Benefits

6. _____ is a method of payment designed to approximate the dentist's actual fee schedule.

   (a) Capitation
   (b) Indemnification
   (c) Schedule of allowances
   (d) UCR

7. "Cosmetic dentistry" and orthodontics are frequent _____ from dental health plans.

   (a) deductibles
   (b) exclusions
   (c) incentive copayments
   (d) riders

8. The _____ is the person representing the family unit in relation to the dental insurance plan.

   (a) beneficiary
   (b) insured
   (c) subscriber
   (d) B or C

9. In UCR plans, a _____ dentist has made a contract with the plan and has usually agreed to prefile his fees and will accept the amount received from the carrier as payment in full.

   (a) nonparticipating
   (b) participating

10. _____ is a provision of an insurance program by which the beneficiary shares in the cost of covered expenses on a percentage basis.

    (a) Assignment
    (b) Coinsurance
    (c) Copayment
    (d) B or C

11. A/an _____ is a stipulated sum which the covered person must pay each year toward the cost of dental treatment before the benefits of the program go into effect.

    (a) annual maximum
    (b) coinsurance
    (c) deductible
    (d) exclusion

12. Coverage commonly ceases within 30 days of the time that the _____.

    (a) carrier changes the rules for eligibility.
    (b) group decides to drop its coverage.
    (c) subscriber stops being a full-time employee.
    (d) B or C

13. A/an _____ is the total dollar amount a dental plan will pay toward the cost of dental care incurred by an individual, or family, in a specified policy year.

    (a) alternative treatment provision
    (b) annual deductible
    (c) annual maximum
    (d) predetermination of benefits

14. After superbill entries have been completed, the _____ copy is given to the patient as his receipt or walk-out statement.

    (a) pink
    (b) white
    (c) yellow
    (d) A, B or C

15. The insurance company that has agreed to provide coverage under a dental plan is known as the _____.

    (a) beneficiary
    (b) carrier
    (c) insured
    (d) subscriber

16. Under an alternative treatment provision, the carrier determines which treatment plan will be used for the patient.

    (a) true
    (b) false

17. _____ is a provision of a group insurance contract stating that when a patient is covered under more than one group dental plan, benefits paid by all plans will be limited to 100% of the actual charges.

    (a) Alternative treatment provision
    (b) Coordination of benefits
    (c) Pre-treatment estimate
    (d) A or C

18. If the patient has paid his account and a check arrives from the insurance carrier, the check is _____.

    (a) credited to the patient's account.
    (b) held in escrow.
    (c) returned to the carrier.
    (d) sent to the patient.

19. A _____ is a list of specific amounts that the carrier will pay toward the cost of dental services rendered.

    (a) schedule of allowances
    (b) schedule of benefits
    (c) table of allowances
    (d) A, B and C

20. Dental benefits _____ included in Medicare coverage.

    (a) are
    (b) are not

21. A/an _____ is an administrative procedure whereby the dentist
    submits the treatment plan to the carrier before treatment is
    started.

    (a) alternative treatment provision
    (b) determination of eligibility
    (c) pre-treatment estimate
    (d) UCR

22. The _____ of the claim form contains actual treatment
    information.

    (a) Attending Dentist's Statement
    (b) dentist section
    (c) patient section
    (d) B and C

23. The ADA procedure codes for restorative services are contained
    in the _____ code series.

    (a) 00100-00999
    (b) 02000-02999
    (c) 04000-04999
    (d) 07000-07999

24. A fee is _____ when it is in the range of the usual fee charges
    for the same service by dentists with similar training and
    experience within a specific and limited geographic or
    socioeconomic area.

    (a) customary
    (b) reasonable
    (c) usual
    (d) A or C

25. _____ affect the amount of coverage and the amount paid under
    the terms of a dental plan.

    (a) Annual maximums
    (b) Coinsurance
    (c) Deductibles
    (d) A, B and C

PROCEDURE: PREPARING AN INSURANCE CLAIM FORM		
GOAL: The student will prepare an insurance claim form based on the following information: Martha Kingsley is the patient. She was born on March 12, 1950 and her Social Security Number is 432-09-0172. She lives at 1221 Oak Hills Road, Anytown, USA. Martha is the subscriber, and Delta Dental is the carrier. The carrier's address is 344 East Dearborn, Chicago, IL. Martha is employed in Allied Engineering in Anytown and the policy (group) number is AE6554. Today Martha had an initial oral examination (procedure code #00110 and the fee was $10), a prophylaxis (procedure code #01110 and the fee was $20).		

SE = Student evaluation C = Criterion met IE = Instructor evaluation X = Criterion not met	SE	IE
1. **Instruments and Materials:** ADA standard insurance claim form, pen and the above information.		
2. Completed all parts of the form with the information available. Form was legible and easy to read.		
3. Identified areas of missing information.		
Comments:		

LEARNING GOALS

The student will be able to:

1. Identify and use the terminology associated with expenses and disbursements.

2. Given the necessary information, establish the reorder point and reorder quantity for a given supply.

3. State the four points to be checked before calling for repair service on a piece of equipment.

4. Describe the procedures for management of accounts payable, C.O.D. deliveries and the petty cash fund.

5. State the proper way to handle a N.S.F. check and describe how to make the necessary adjustments on the office bookkeeping systems.

6. Identify the payroll taxes that: are withheld from payroll checks, require a matching contribution by the employer, and which are paid only by the employer.

7. Demonstrate writing a check and making a check register entry.

EXERCISES

1. _____ income minus payment of all practice-related expenses yields the dentist's net income.

   (a) Fixed
   (b) Gross
   (c) Net
   (d) Variable

2. Infrequent, small office expenses are paid from the _____ fund.

   (a) change
   (b) C.O.D.
   (c) disbursement
   (d) petty cash

3. A _____ notice is sent to a customer to advise him that an item is not available for delivery with the balance of the order.

    (a) back order
    (b) debit memo
    (c) purchase order
    (d) reorder memo

4. If lost or stolen, a check signed with a _____ endorsement cannot be cashed.

    (a) blanket
    (b) dated
    (c) personal
    (d) restrictive

5. The reorder point for any supply is based on the _____ and the necessary lead time.

    (a) back order
    (b) inventory system
    (c) rate of use
    (d) reorder quantity

6. A/an _____ is a formal application or order for supplies.

    (a) acquisition
    (b) inventory control
    (c) purchase order
    (d) requisition

7. A/an _____ is a supply which is literally "used up" as part of its function.

    (a) consumable
    (b) disposable
    (c) expendable
    (d) A and B

8. _____ include(s) those business expenses which continue at all times whether or not the dentist is working.

    (a) Accounts payable
    (b) Accounts receivable
    (c) Fixed overhead
    (d) Variable overhead

Match the following terms and definitions

9. _____ Canceled checks

(a) Items, other than canceled checks, that have been deducted directly from the account.

10. _____ Debits

(b) Not sufficient funds check.

11. _____ Deposits in transit

(c) All checks that have been written and paid against the account.

12. _____ Outstanding checks

(d) Deposits that have been made but are not yet credited to the account.

(e) Checks that have been written but not yet paid by the bank.

13. _____ is not a Federal payroll deduction.

(a) FICA
(b) Income tax
(c) Social Security
(d) Worker's Compensation

14. Fifty dollars is normally kept in the petty cash fund. There is now $15.23 in cash and receipts for $34.77. A check for _____ must be written to replenish the fund.

(a) $15.23
(b) $19.54
(c) $34.77
(d) $50.00

15. Before calling for repair service you should check the _____.

(a) electrical plug
(b) fuse
(c) reset button
(d) A, B and C

16. _____ is a payroll deduction that requires a matching contribution by the employer.

   (a) FICA
   (b) FUTA
   (c) Income tax
   (d) A and B

17. Within 30 days of the end of the calendar year, or upon termination of employment, the employee must be furnished with a/an _____ form.

   (a) Circular E
   (b) income tax
   (c) W-2
   (d) W-4

18. The _____ is the person named on the check as the intended recipient of the amount shown.

   (a) bearer
   (b) maker
   (c) payee
   (d) payer

19. The reorder quantity is the _____ quantity of a product to be ordered at one time.

   (a) maximum
   (b) minimum

20. A/an _____ is a form authorizing the purchase of specific supplies from a specific supplier.

   (a) invoice
   (b) packing slip
   (c) purchase order
   (d) requisition

21. A stop payment order must be given in writing.

   (a) true
   (b) false

22. If a returned check cannot be redeposited, the amount of the check must be _____ the bank balance and income figures.

   (a) added to
   (b) subtracted from

23. At least once every _____ the employee should request a "Statement of Earnings" from the Social Security Administration.

   (a) 6 months
   (b) 2 years
   (c) 3 years
   (d) 5 years

24. The bank statement and _____ should be reconciled promptly upon receipt of the statement.

   (a) accounts payable records
   (b) check register
   (c) expense records
   (d) A and C

25. Net pay _____ deductions must equal earned gross pay.

   (a) minus
   (b) plus

PROCEDURE: CHECK WRITING		
GOAL: The student will demonstrate writing a check and completing the check register entry for a check in payment of the following invoice. The doctor owes ABC Supply Company $87.23 for dental supplies. This invoice is to be paid in full.		
SE = Student evaluation C = Criterion met IE = Instructor evaluation X = Criterion not met	SE	IE
1. **Instruments and Materials:** a blank check and check register (or simulation) and a pen.		
2. Made the check register entry first in ink.		
3. Completed the check ready for signature.		
Comments:		

LEARNING GOALS

The student will be able to:

1. Describe the role of the dental auxiliary when employed as a generalist, administrative assistant, chairside or coordinating assistant, EFDA, office manager and dental auxiliary educator.

2. Discuss what she wants in a job and what she has to offer a potential employer.

3. List at least three places where an auxiliary seeking employment may look for information.

4. Describe the responsibilities of both the employer and employee in maintaining employment.

5. Demonstrate preparing a personal resume and letter of application.

EXERCISES

1. A private employment agency charges a fee if it finds you a position. _____ responsible for paying this fee.

   (a) You are
   (b) Your new employer is

2. References _____ be included as part of your résumé.

   (a) should
   (b) should not

Match the following:

3. _____ Administrative
         assistant

   (a) Performs reversible procedures
       providing these duties are in
       compliance with the state's
       dental practice act.

4. _____ Chairside
         assistant

   (b) Is primarily responsible for
       the smooth and efficient
       operation of the business
       office.

5. ____ Coordinating
        assistant

   (c) Is responsible for working
       with the dentist in the
       treatment area.

6. ____ Generalist

   (d) Has specific responsibilities of
       her own and may "help out" as
       needed elsewhere in the office.

7. _____ Expanded Function
         Dental Assistant

   (e) Is responsible for the office
       preventive dentistry program.

   (f) Is responsible for all dental
       assisting functions in the
       practice where she is the only
       assistant.

8. A/an _____ is a legal arrangement between two or more persons
   having equal rights and duties.

   (a) expense-sharing arrangement
   (b) partnership
   (c) professional association
   (d) professional corporation

9. An assistant interested in working in a veterans' hospital
   should apply to the area _____.

   (a) Bureau of Veterans' Affairs.
   (b) Civil Service Office.
   (c) Director of Personnel.
   (d) A and C

10. Most schools require _____ as the minimal educational level for a dental auxiliary teacher.

    (a) a bachelor's degree
    (b) CPR certification
    (c) current certification
    (d) state registration

11. A letter of application, enclosed with a resume, _____ include personal information.

    (a) should
    (b) should not

12. Personal data on a resume must include race, color, religion, sex, national origin and marital status.

    (a) true
    (b) false

13. When completing a paper and pencil personnel test it is important that you _____.

    (a) finish within the time allowed.
    (b) follow directions exactly.
    (c) print neatly.
    (d) use a pen.

14. A/an _____ is a written document that clarifies the terms of employment.

    (a) contract
    (b) employment agreement
    (c) job description
    (d) office procedures manual

15. Most employers routinely consider the first several weeks as a _____ period during which either party may terminate the relationship without notice.

    (a) conditional
    (b) probationary
    (c) training
    (d) trial

16. Stealing, use of drugs or any other form of unprofessional
    behavior are considered cause for _____.

    (a) conditional dismissal
    (b) salary reduction
    (c) summary dismissal
    (d) termination

17. The EFDA is responsible to _____ for providing care that is best
    for the patient's well-being.

    (a) herself
    (b) the dentist
    (c) the patient
    (d) A, B and C

18. The _____ assumes many supervisory and managerial
    responsibilities.

    (a) administrative assistant
    (b) dental hygienist
    (c) EFDA
    (d) office manager

19. _____ is a special form of insurance that reimburses the
    employer for a loss resulting from theft of funds by an
    employee.

    (a) Bonding
    (b) Expense-sharing
    (c) Incorporation
    (d) Professional association

20. When you telephone in response to a newspaper classified ad, you
    should be able to speak to the dentist to find out more about
    the job.

    (a) true
    (b) false

21. You _____ wear your dental assisting uniform to the interview.

    (a) should
    (b) should not

22. It is proper to list _____ as references.

    (a) former employers
    (b) friends
    (c) relatives
    (d) A and C

23. Bright red nail polish _____ appropriate for the dental office.

    (a) is
    (b) is not

24. A neat uniformed appearance includes _____.

    (a) a bow to keep hair back
    (b) a wrist watch
    (c) the association pin
    (d) B and C

25. The benefits to the auxiliary of being an employee of a larger
    group include _____.

    (a) the opportunity to develop more specialized skills.
    (b) the potential for a more extensive program of employee
        benefits.
    (c) the professional stimulation and sociability of working with
        many other auxiliaries.
    (d) A, B and C

PROCEDURE: PREPARING A RÉSUMÉ		
GOAL: The student will prepare a personal résumé for use in seeking employment.		
SE = Student evaluation C = Criterion met IE = Instructor evaluation X = Criterion not met	SE	IE
1. **Instruments and Materials:** Plain paper, typewriter or pen.		
2. Prepared a résumé including the following parts: personal directory, objective, work experience, education, other activities, and personal data.		
3. Résumé was neat and professional in appearance and was free of misspelled words.		
Comments:		

PROCEDURE: WRITING A LETTER OF APPLICATION		
GOAL: The student will write a letter of application, in modified block style, to accompany her resumé. The letter is being sent in response to a classified advertisement in The Daily Times newspaper.		
SE = Student evaluation C = Criterion met IE = Instructor evaluation X = Criterion not met	SE	IE
1. **Instruments and Materials**: plain paper, typewriter or pen.		
2. The letter contained appropriate information and was free of misspelled words.		
3. The letter was in modified block style and neat in appearance.		
Comments:		

NOTES

NOTES

NOTES

NOTES

NOTES

NOTES

NOTES

NOTES

NOTES

NOTES